This book might well become essential reading for any teacher desiring to understand a child's developing sense of number. Richardson has taken complex ideas about number development and translated those ideas for teachers using practical, common sense terms in detailed description. Since Common Core was first published we have heard talk of progressions, trajectories and learning continua, often hard to translate for practical implementation by teachers. But Richardson transforms the complexity by introducing "Critical Learning Phases"; obviously gleaned from observed behaviors of many children. In this easy to decipher text she offers teachers a treasure trove of ideas to help alleviate the confusion many teachers feel about teaching math. Richardson steers the reader towards some practical understandings. And she rightly warns us how "Sometimes the indicators that reveal whether or not a child understands the mathematics are overlooked, because in certain situations, he or she appears to know. So, assumptions are made that children know more about the concept than they do." This warning nicely captures why it would be wise for all K, 1, and 2 teachers to read Richardson's thoughts and practical interpretations on number related learning.

Hal Melnick, PhD
Bank Street College of Education NYC
Leadership in Mathematics Education

*I have used Kathy Richardson's **Assessing Math Concepts** interviews with students over many years. I think they are very powerful tool for identifying crucial missing links in mathematical knowledge. Now, with this new book, I have the background knowledge in one place to read and study. It is a great addition to Kathy's work.*

Susan Friel, Ed.D
Professor of Mathematics Education
The University of North Carolina at Chapel Hill

How Children Learn Number Concepts

How do we help children develop the foundation necessary for future mathematical success? With clarity and eloquence, Kathy Richardson answers this question by illuminating the complexity of the intellectual work young children must do in order to build a robust sense of number. She identifies critical phases in the development of understandings in core topics such as counting and place value and provides examples that bring to life their importance for future mathematics learning. At a time when policy makers expect children to learn mathematics concepts and skills at earlier and earlier ages, this book should give teachers the courage to spend the time necessary for children to develop numerical understandings strong enough to provide a solid foundation for, rather than illusions of, learning.

Cathy Humphreys, Doctoral Student, Stanford University
Co-author of *Connecting Mathematical Ideas* with Jo Boaler
Co-author of *A Collection of Math Lessons, Grades 6-8* with Marilyn Burns

Through her extensive research of interviewing thousands of children, Kathy Richardson discovered children go through predictable stages on their way to learning number concepts. She identifies these stages as "phases" and "critical" because of their importance. During this transition time toward implementation of the Common Core Standards in Mathematics, **How Children Learn Number Concepts: A Guide to the Critical Learning Phases** *is a must have for teachers working with young children in number. She unpacks content as well as the learning journey for children acquiring number and number concepts. The Guide is clear and concise while giving guidance to empower me, as a teacher, to understand and in that understanding to meet the growth needs of students.*

Sheri Willebrand, President
California Mathematics Council

I hope every teacher of young children, every parent, every administrator and every educational policy maker will read this book. Kathy has studied children's thinking about mathematics for decades and has now written a book that will help us all understand the critical stages of development in young children's thinking that are essential to building a solid foundation for numerical reasoning.

Educational policymakers will come to understand the complexity of the ideas that young children encounter in thinking about number, and they, and we, will better understand that pushing abstract mathematical ideas too early in the grades can actually undermine children's efforts to come to know and understand numbers and our number system.

As a grandparent, I learned a lot from this book about where to focus while helping my grandchildren with early number concepts. This book is a wonderful gift to teachers and parents alike who want to help young children make sense of early number concepts.

Ruth Parker, CEO of Mathematics Education
Collaborative (MEC)

Kathy Richardson has provided us a wonderful explanation of how children acquire early skills and conceptual understanding of number. This book offers teachers and interventionists the crucial background information to understand what children REALLY know and what we ASSUME they know.

It is only with this magnified examination that we can "move" children along in their mathematical competencies or help them fill the gaps that have long brought them misconceptions. Making use of the information in this book should help teachers of young children be much more knowledgeable about the real meaning of mastery.

Patsy Kanter
Author, *Every Day Counts, Calendar Math and Partner Games,
Summer Success: Math, USDE Helping Your Child Learn Math*

This is a wonderful, in-depth explanation of how children learn beginning number concepts and how they should be taught if children are to have some depth, rather than superficial understanding, of the mathematics behind them. I think this book would be very valuable for the experienced teachers of young students as well as new teachers, in helping to shape their understanding of early mathematics learning. This book could act as a guide in their teaching, choice of curriculum, and assessment of students' basic of number concepts.

The organization by Critical Learning Phases is logical and progressive. This path through the chapters provides a step-by-step understanding that learning about number is like building with blocks—as the building grows, each building block below is important for those that are added on top.

Paul Giganti, Jr.
Coordinator of Public Programs for Graduate School of Education
University of California, Berkeley
Author, *Each Orange Had 8 Slices*

How Children Learn Number Concepts

A Guide to the Critical Learning Phases

Kathy Richardson

Math Perspectives
Teacher Development Center

Math Perspectives Teacher Development Center
PO Box 29418
Bellingham, WA 98228
www.mathperspectives.com

Distributed by Didax, Inc.

Didax
395 Main Street
Rowley, MA 01969-1207
(800) 458-0024
www.didax.com

E F G H I 20 19 18 17 16

ISBN 978-0-9848381-9-6

Editor: Teresa Schmidt
Cover design: Three Sixty Productions
Interior design: Three Sixty Productions
Production Coordinator: JoEllen Key

Printed in the United States of America on recycled, acid-free paper

Table of Contents

FOREWORD

T his book was written to help Pre-K though 4th educators recognize the complexities of the mathematics young children are expected to learn, and to identify what is required for children to develop an understanding of number concepts. The information is also useful for those who work with older children who do not yet have the foundation necessary for success.

The Critical Leaning Phases, identified here, are not skills that can be directly taught to children. Rather, they are the understandings that must be in place if children are going to be successful in the study of mathematics. Children develop understandings of the Critical Learning Phases through instruction that builds on what they already know and understand.

The Critical Learning Phases are often unrecognized or assumed to be in place as children move through the math curriculum. This means many children do not have key prerequisite understandings in place before they receive instruction. They may appear to be successful in the short term but their lack of meaningful learning eventually shows up. This leads to many children believing they are failures in math. Much of their time and energy is spent on trying to learn certain procedures when what they really need is the foundation on which the procedures are based.

Children who do not expect math to make sense simply guess or try to remember what the teacher said. These children look at the teacher to see if they are right, rather than to their own ability to think and make sense.

Children will learn MORE in the long run when they are provided the instruction they need, rather than given extra time to study what they are not yet able to learn with meaning. Children who expect math to make sense will puzzle over what they don't understand, ask questions and try things out to see what happens. They are persistent and work to make sense. I have yet to meet a child who is not "tickled" when they figure something out that challenges them—but is also within reach.

Teachers can maximize what children learn if they know what level of thinking they have developed, and what they still need to understand regarding a particular concept. Teachers will be able to recognize the difference between getting their students to do or say something that gives the appearance of knowledge and evidence that shows they really know.

It is possible to meet each child's needs within a classroom setting even though the children are not all working at the same level. This is because within whatever larger concept the children are learning, there are levels of understanding. So for example, if a class is working on comparing numbers, some children will be able to find the differences between numbers to 20, and others will need to work with numbers to 10 and identify only which number is more and which is less than the other. If children are working with place value, some children will be just beginning to understand how to count tens as units, and other children will be combining numbers to make all the tens they can.

Just as children read at different levels, children can work on math concepts at different levels. What is key is that the child is making real progress and not trying to do what they are told without insight.

ACKNOWLEDGEMENTS

This work is the culmination of more than 40 years working with children and teachers: observing, wondering, discussing, reading, and thinking. I have been helped, challenged and enlightened by interactions with so many over the years that it is impossible to list all who have been part of this journey.

This is to all the children and teachers who accompanied me along the way and to my family who gave me undying support every step of the way.

Thanks to all of you.

Kathy

Introduction

The Critical Learning Phases:
Key to Effective Instruction

THE CRITICAL LEARNING PHASES:
Key To Effective Instruction

I have been intrigued with the study of how children learn mathematics for more than forty years, beginning when I taught my first class of 36 unforgettable first graders.

Since then, I have worked with children from pre-school through sixth grade, and in the field of special education—both in my own classroom, and alongside teachers who shared their students with me. Over the years, I have interacted with children in many regions of this country and others. I have analyzed children's responses, seeking to delve deeper into their thinking to determine how they perceived the problems I gave them, and how they interpreted various mathematical situations.

I found there are crucial mathematical ideas that students must understand if they are to find meaning in the mathematics they are expected to learn. I call these understandings "Critical Learning Phases." The term "critical" is used to underscore the essential role each level or phase has on how children make sense of numbers and thus, what mathematics they are able (or not) to learn. Critical Learning Phases are the understandings that must be in place to ensure that children are not just imitating procedures or saying words they don't really understand. They are milestones, or hurdles, in children's growth of understanding; they are insights, rather than facts or procedures.

Children can learn to answer questions and follow procedures, yet lack the level of awareness that gives real meaning to the math. For example, a child may be able to line up 12 counters, carefully touch each one, and tell the teacher how many she counted. But we cannot say she understands what she needs to know about counting unless she can also count out 12 objects. Can she keep the 12 in mind or will she count right past it? Another child may have memorized "6 and 6 is 12," but can he use what he knows to solve 6 + 7? A child may have learned that 3 tens and 4 is 34, but if 10 more are added, can he tell how many there are without counting?

Whether a child understands a Critical Learning Phase can be determined by asking questions or observing behaviors. A child who understands a Critical Learning Phase finds the answer(s) to be obvious. Children who do not yet understand respond in ways that reveal their level of thinking.

When children are taught mathematical concepts or procedures before they reach certain levels of thinking, they do not see the underlying logic of the mathematics they are working with. All they can do is memorize processes and procedures. It may appear that they know the mathematics, but in reality, this is just an illusion. What they have learned is not useful to them because they cannot build on it. This "illusion of learning" breaks down at the point where true understanding is necessary for further growth.

If we are to ensure that children have learned the foundational mathematics they need as they move on to higher levels, educators must be aware of the development of the Critical Learning Phases and the indicators that reveal what children do and do not understand. If we look only at the ability to get right answers, we miss the information needed to determine what children know and still need to learn. The result is that children spend valuable instructional time trying to memorize what doesn't make sense to them, instead of developing the understandings they need.

The Critical Learning Phases presented here focus on number concepts. The development of number concepts is the foundation and heart of the mathematics program for young children. What children know and understand about number and number relationships impacts every other area of mathematical study. Children cannot analyze data, determine functional relationships, compare measures of area and volume, or describe relative lengths of sides unless they can use numbers in meaningful ways. Number concepts are the foundation that children must have in order to achieve high standards in mathematics as a whole.

Children who understand number concepts know that numbers are used to describe quantities and relationships, and are useful tools for getting information about the world they live in. They see relationships between numbers, and can take numbers apart and put them back together without counting. They understand the structure of numbers and think of numbers as made up of groups of tens and ones, or hundreds, tens and ones, and so forth. They know what happens to the numbers when they add, subtract, multiply, or divide. They use symbols to represent numerical ideas, and can explain and interpret what the symbols mean. They are able to think with numbers, and to use numerical ideas to analyze situations and solve a variety of problems. They work with numbers with facility and ease, and demonstrate proficiency with computation.

When children are given instruction at an appropriate level that helps them focus on meaning and relationships, they are

---

able to accomplish remarkable things. Learning to compute becomes a significant part of their study of mathematics, and helps them develop mathematical thinking and reasoning. In addition to learning how to add, subtract, multiply, and divide, children also learn number relationships, number composition and decomposition, and the principles underlying the structure of the number system. In other words, they are not only competent when dealing with computational problems, but they will also know more mathematics.

Each chapter in the book covers basic concepts and ideas that must be understood if children are going to learn the underlying structure of numbers and how to add, subtract, multiply, and divide with meaning and competence. We look closely at the kinds of thinking children do as they work with these core concepts, and learn to recognize the many stages of thinking that reveal the growth of understanding that occurs over time.

All children progress through certain levels of understanding, albeit at different times, and often without adults' awareness. For example, when children first learn to add numbers like 3 and 4, they think of this as "1 and 1 and 1," and another group of "1 and 1 and 1 and 1." The only way they know to determine the answer is to count all the objects. Later, they will recognize three objects without needing to count them, and will be able to start with 3 and count on to 7. Subsequently, they will more often see that 4 is composed of 3 and 1, and will be able to use the idea that 3 and 3 are 6, so 3 and 4 must be 7. Eventually, they will know that 3 and 4 are 7 without having to think about it. If teachers ignore these stages and just ask the children to memorize the words "three plus four equals seven," they are, in effect, asking them to learn a "song," rather than learn the important relationships these words describe.

At every stage of development, the size of the numbers and the size of the differences between numbers influences what the child is able to understand. That is, a child may be able to see that 5 is contained in 7, but not yet know how 15 is related to 17. Or a child may know the parts of numbers to 4, but not how to figure out the parts of 6.

The level of abstractness also affects what children are able to think about. Children develop a true sense of number by working with real things, rather than with symbols. As children develop their understanding of number, they begin with models, moving them to aid their thinking. They generally advance from being able to think about numbers when they can actually move objects, to thinking about relationships when the model is present but not touched, to thinking about relationships without a physical model. After children can work with an idea at all of these levels, their work with the symbolic representations of this idea will have meaning. Even then, young children rarely reach the level of totally abstract thinking. When working with symbols, they usually need to be thinking of some concrete referent.

Each stage of learning is much more complex than is generally recognized. If we look at counting, for example, we will see that children who are competent counters have integrated several major ideas about counting. These include one-to-one correspondence, inclusion, keeping track, remembering how many, and knowing one more and one less. A child who understands counting will be able to keep track of an unorganized group of objects and will also be able to count out a particular quantity from a larger group of objects. Children who understand place value are able to think of ten as a collection of 10 ones, at the same time they think of the ten as a unit of 1. They are able to think of 180 ones as 18 tens, or 1 hundred and 8 tens.

This deep understanding of number concepts and relationships does not develop quickly. Children need ongoing and multiple opportunities to develop number sense: to count and compare quantities, to add and subtract, to work with place value in ways that ask them to think and reason, to see relationships, and to make connections. We need to provide children with the kinds of experiences that will help them confront the complexity of these ideas, and encourage them to think and make sense of them.

If we are going to raise achievement in mathematics in ways that allow children to build on what they know, and thus maintain high levels of achievement throughout their schooling, teachers must focus on the mathematics they want children to learn—not on whether they are able to get right answers. Once teachers have identified what children really know and what they need to learn, they will be able to provide appropriate instruction that will give children a solid foundation on which to build, ensuring success for all students.

In the following chapters, we will look at each core topic basic to children's understanding of number. We will identify and describe the Critical Learning Phases within that topic, which must be in place if children are going to build foundational understandings.

Chapter One

Understanding Counting

UNDERSTANDING COUNTING

C ounting is more than reciting a rote sequence and recognizing numerals. Counting is finding out "how many." Often, parents and teachers are more focused on how high a child can go in saying the counting sequence than on the number of objects the child can actually count. Because children can learn the language and patterns of counting long before they understand what counting is all about, it is assumed that a child knows how to use counting to determine the number of objects.

When we watch young children count, we begin to realize they do not yet see numbers the same way as adults. They do not trust that quantities remain the same when they are rearranged. They are not necessarily aware that they must keep track of which objects have or have not already been counted. Young children do not yet understand that when a group of objects looks different (for example, the counters are spread out or pushed together), the quantity remains the same. They think they have more if their sandwich is cut into four pieces instead of two pieces, and are not sure what happens to the quantity of objects if they are hidden. They may also believe there are more chairs than pencils, because the pencils are smaller. Young children work diligently to "count right," but are unable to tell if what they have ended up with is a reasonable or unreasonable amount.

Count and Land

When children first learn to count, they think of quantities as a series of one, and another one, and another one, and so on. In a sense, they are labeling each counter rather than determining how many there are altogether. Their focus is on touching each object and saying the right numbers. Their answer is whatever number they happen to land on when they have finished pointing at each object. I refer to this stage as the "Count and Land" stage.

Developing a Sense of Quantity

There is more to counting, however, than landing on the right number. Children grapple with many complex ideas far beyond "saying their numbers" and getting the right answer. They must develop an understanding of how numbers work and learn the meanings of the quantities they are working with. Children need to learn to tell when an answer is reasonable or not reasonable, and to be consistent and accurate when counting. They need to see relationships between numbers and use these relationships to find out about other numbers.

Most of all, children need to believe that numbers make sense and that they can make sense of them. This is not something easily attained—and certainly not mastered in the first year or two of school—but it is that search for the sense of number that is worthy of the child's time.

Learning to Count Objects

Counting is a complex concept—the integration of several important ideas. Children need to understand all of the related Critical Learning Phases before we can be sure they understand what counting is all about. Children move through several stages of thinking as they develop an understanding of the Critical Learning Phases. We need to be cognizant of stages of thinking that reveal their lack of understanding as well as those that reveal the level of proficiency they have reached.

When determining which Critical Learning Phase a child has reached, the size of the number must be taken into consideration. For example, a child may be able to count out a pile of 9 but not be able to count out a pile of 18. A child may know how many he counted after counting a pile of 12, but not remember where he landed after counting a pile of 32. A child may be able to tell one less without counting for numbers to 5, but just guess when asked to tell one less from 20.

The following Critical Learning Phases identify what is crucial for children to learn as they develop a deep understanding of counting:

Counting Objects

- Counts one item for each number (one-to one correspondence)
- Keeps track of an unorganized pile
- Notices when recounting a group results in a different number
- Is bothered when counting a group results in the same number after some have been added or taken away
- Spontaneously checks by recounting to see if the result is the same
- Knows "how many" after counting
- Counts out a particular quantity
- Reacts to estimate while counting
- Spontaneously adjusts estimate while counting and makes a closer estimate

Knowing One More/One Less

- Knows one more in sequence without counting
- Knows one less in sequence without counting
- Notices if a counting pattern doesn't make sense *(Ex: instead of saying "13, 12, 11," says "13, 14, 15," or instead of saying "21, 22, 23", says "20, 30, 40")*

- Knows one more without counting when numbers are presented out of sequence
- Knows one less without counting when numbers are presented out of sequence

Counting Objects by Groups

- Counts by groups by moving the appropriate group of counters
- Knows quantity stays the same when counted by different-sized groups

Using Symbols

- Uses numerals to describe quantities

COUNTING OBJECTS

- **Counts one item for each number word (one-to-one correspondence)**

When young children first attempt to count, they are not aware that they need to touch one object for each number word they say. They only know that they are supposed to point at the objects while they say the counting sequence. So, when children point and count without touching each counter, they are acting out counting, but they don't yet understand what counting is about. When they become aware that they must touch one counter for each counting number they say, they are at the beginning stage of learning to count.

It is interesting to note that counting one-to-one is not all or nothing. Children may have one-to-one counting for numbers to 10, for example, and then begin to lose focus when the numbers get larger.

Children who understand this Critical Learning Phase touch one counter each time they say a number.

■ Keeps track of an unorganized pile

Even after children become aware that they need to count one-to-one, many do not realize that each object must be counted once and only once. They try to touch one counter for each number they say, but do not pay much attention to which counters they have and have not touched, so they miss some or count some more than once. They don't see that they need a system for keeping track.

When children have developed systems for keeping track and are consistent in a variety of situations, including counting things that cannot be moved (like pictures), it can be said that they can keep track.

Children who are aware that they need to keep track will not always be accurate. They may count correctly when they start out and then lose track as they go. They may be off by just one or two because they missed or recounted one or two objects. Sometimes they are off because they skipped saying a number. At this stage, they understand what they need to do, but because they find the task difficult, they are inconsistent.

Developing ease and consistency is a major task for the beginning counter. Children need lots of practice until counting becomes easy for them and they can use counting as a tool for determining quantities in a variety of situations.

How Children Learn Number Concepts

Children who understand this Critical Learning Phase consistently touch each item once and only once when they count.

■ Notices when recounting a group results in a different number

■ Is bothered when counting a group results in the same number after some have been added or taken away

If counting is going to be a meaningful task, children need to understand why keeping track matters. When children do not fully understand, it won't bother them if they end up with different amounts when recounting the same group of objects. Teachers need to be aware of and look for the behaviors that indicate whether or not children understand the need to keep track.

We see Ester's lack of understanding in the following example: Ester counted a pile of objects and found she had 8. Her teacher added one more to the pile. Ester did not know how many counters were now in the pile, so she counted them and got the same number 8 again. She commented, "Oh. Eight again." It was interesting to her, but not impossible! She was not inclined to think she might not have kept track accurately, because it did not bother her to land on the same number after one more had been added.

We cannot fully determine whether children completely understand the need to keep track unless we observe them in several settings to see how they handle situations when they are inaccurate. Do they notice? Are they bothered? Do they check and see?

Children who understand these Critical Learning Phases react if it doesn't make sense to end up with the number they did when they counted.

■ Spontaneously checks by recounting to see if the result is the same

As understanding grows and children recognize that they should get the same number every time they count a particular group of objects, they will start checking to see if they actually do come up with the same number each time. This is different than checking in order to be right, and because the teacher says so—it is a spontaneous action as they verify for themselves how numbers work.

It is a sign of growth when this need to check comes from their own developing awareness and not because an adult has told them to check.

Children who understand this Critical Learning Phase pay attention to what they counted and spontaneously double-check to make sure they land on the same number again.

■ Knows "how many" after counting

Another important aspect of counting goes beyond being accurate to developing a sense of quantity. Children move through several stages while developing an awareness of quantity. At a very early stage of counting, children do not know how many they counted, even immediately after they finish counting. This is an indication that their attention was not on the quantity, but on the action of counting. The number they landed on had no meaning for them and they don't remember what they said. Some children will guess or say they don't know, others will recount to find out. When they recount in order to answer the question, they usually pay more attention to the last number they said, if they can.

The child who knows "how many?" after counting is more aware of the purpose of counting. The child is thinking about what she is trying to find out, and not just on landing at the right place.

Children who understand this Critical Learning Phase respond to the question "how many?" with the number they landed on when they counted, without needing to recount to find out.

■ Counts out a particular quantity

Counting out a particular quantity is an entirely different process than counting a given group of objects. There are two types of situations that require children to count out a quantity. One is when someone asks them to get a specific number of items: "Would you get 9 paper plates?" The other is when they have to determine the number themselves in order to get enough for everyone: "Would you get a paper plate for everyone in your group?"

Counting out a particular number requires children to hold the number in their mind while they are counting. This means the number must have enough meaning to them that they can remember it while they are counting. When the quantity has little or no meaning for them, they don't hold that amount in their mind and count past what has been asked for. The next stage is when they hear themselves say the number asked for as they count, and are reminded that they are supposed to count out that particular number. At this point, they will be able to spontaneously self-correct and start over, or fix their mistake. Over time, the numbers begin to have meaning for children, and they develop the ability to hold a number in mind and easily count out the number requested.

When children are asked to get an undetermined number of objects for a specific situation, their first attempts will be on getting "one for you," and "one for you," and "one for you," rather than on getting a total amount. When children are able to determine the number needed and count out the right amount all at once, they will have moved beyond thinking of numbers as one and one and one, and think of 9 children and 9 paper plates as the same number.

Children who understand this Critical Learning Phase can easily and consistently count out a particular quantity.

■ Reacts to estimate while counting

It takes a long time for young children to develop a sense of quantities and relationships. There are several ways that we can get some indication about how meaningful numbers are becoming for the children. One way to gain insight into a child's sense of number is to ask the child to estimate before counting a group of objects. This particular Critical Learning Phase is not about the ability to estimate per se, but children's ability to attend to what they are counting in light of what they estimated.

Children move though stages as they begin to develop an ability to think about quantity at the same time they are focused on keeping track of what they are counting. When asked to estimate, young children will often say whatever number comes to mind. They do not have enough experiences to make a reasonable estimate. We can tell they are just saying any number, because many times children say a number without even looking at the group of objects they are to count.

Young children will often count without paying any attention to their estimate. This generally means the number was more of a guess than an estimate, and not very meaningful to the child. Children who are thinking about what they are finding out as they count, will react or comment. For example, they might hesitate when they reach the number they said, or they might say, "I guess it's not 20," when they finish counting.

Children who understand this Critical Learning Phase realize when they have counted past or won't reach their estimate. This is not an expectation for young children, but is worth noting when a child has reached this level of awareness. It is also a reminder that learning to count involves more than getting the right answer.

■ Spontaneously adjusts estimate while counting and makes a closer estimate

Numbers do not yet have enough meaning to the beginning counter for them to adjust their estimate while counting. It will be noteworthy if they even react to their estimate as described above. However, over time, as children develop meaning for numbers and focus on what they are learning when they count, they will reach this Critical Leaning Phase. At first they will change their minds about an estimate for very small numbers. For example, a child might be determining the length of a piece of yarn using paper clips to measure. He might estimate that it would take 5 paper clips. Then when he sees that 3 paper clips go almost to the end of the yarn, he might say, "Oh, now I think it will be 4."

Eventually, children develop more meaning for numbers and number relationships. In this example, Baylee is finding out how many walnuts would fit in a jar. She estimates that 40 walnuts would fill the jar. She places walnuts into the jar, counting as she goes. "I have 12 walnuts so far and the jar is almost half full. Wait—I changed my mind—I think it will hold 20 walnuts." It is only after many experiences with larger numbers and looking for number relationships that children will be able to make and adjust estimates.

Children who understand this Critical Learning Phase change their mind and make a closer estimate while they are counting because they have more information on which to base their estimate.

KNOWING ONE MORE/ONE LESS

The long-range goal for children in primary grades is to learn how to add, subtract, multiply, and divide without having to count each item. The first step toward "knowing without counting" is knowing one more and one less. This will eventually be a key idea when working with addition and subtraction.

The size of the number is a big factor in whether a child knows one more or one less than a number. Typically, children learn one more before they learn one less within a particular range of numbers.

■ Knows one more in sequence without counting

The youngest children who are learning to count do not trust numbers enough to believe that it is possible to know how many there will be before they count. Once they realize that one more is the same as "what number comes next," the task primarily becomes a matter of becoming familiar with the counting patterns.

Children who understand this Critical Learning Phase trust they know how many without counting, and know the required number in the one more number sequence.

■ Knows one less in sequence without counting

It is much more difficult for children to tell how many there are when one counter at a time is removed than when one is added, because the one less pattern is much more difficult to learn. It is harder for young children to think about what came before than what comes next.

Children who understand this Critical Learning Phase trust they know how many without counting and know the required number in the one less number sequence.

- **Notices if a counting pattern doesn't make sense**
  *(Ex: instead of saying "13, 12, 11," says "13, 14, 15,"
  or instead of saying "21, 22, 23," says "20, 30, 40")*
  We can't tell how meaningful the one more and one less sequences are for children when they are correct; but we can tell the numbers are not very meaningful if children don't notice when they start using a sequence that doesn't make sense.

  This is especially evident when children are taking one away from numbers starting at 20 down to 10. The sequence does not follow other familiar patterns, and children either count each time to find out how many are left, or use whatever counting pattern comes to mind, even if it doesn't make sense. If children are repeatedly asked to take one away and tell how many are left, it is common for them to start counting forward, even when removing counters. They might say something like: "14, 15, 16, 17," or they slip into other familiar patterns and say things like, "16, 15, 20, 25, 30," or "21, 20, 30, 40, 50." When children become aware that they don't know one less and recount to find out, they are operating at a higher level than when they guess. When children use whatever pattern comes to mind, whether it makes sense or not, it calls into question the meaning number words have for them.

  Children who understand this Critical Learning Phase catch themselves if they slip into a number pattern that doesn't work for the situation. It is not an expectation for the youngest children just learning about numbers to notice this, but it is necessary for children to eventually reach this level of understanding if they are going to make sense of what they are learning.

■ Knows one more without counting when numbers are presented out of sequence

If knowing one more is to become a useful tool for children, they need to be able to tell how many when one more is added to any number. Children develop this ability as the numbers come to have meaning.

Children who understand this Critical Learning Phase can say what number is one more than any other number within the range of numbers they are working with.

■ Knows one less without counting when numbers are presented out of sequence

When numbers come to have meaning to the children, they will be able to tell how many will be left when one is taken away, no matter what order the numbers are presented in.

Children who understand this Critical Learning Phase can say what number is one less than any other number, within the range of numbers they are working with.

COUNTING OBJECTS BY GROUPS

■ Counts by groups by moving the appropriate group of counters

Children are often asked to count by groups by saying a sequence of numbers, for example, "2, 4, 6, 8, 10," without actually counting anything. This practice leads to misconceptions for many children about what this means.

When these children are asked to count a pile of objects by 2s or 5s, for example, they will move one object at a time as they say the sequence. This misconception is reinforced when children count nickels or dimes because they move one object as they count by 5s or 10s.

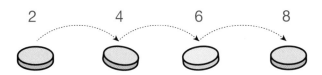

Counting by 2's but moving only one counter for each word.

Many children are confused when asked to count by groups (usually 2s) if they are at the Count and Land stage or before they are totally confident counting by ones. Some will try to arrange the objects they are counting into groups, but then count these groups by 1s or a combination of 1s and 2s, or whatever group they are using. They try to do what they saw the teacher model but do not understand what is intended.

Before children understand that counting by groups is a shortcut for counting by ones, they make the groups of 2, for example, before they count by 2s. Then they point at each group as they say the sequence, "2, 4, 6..." This is a stage along the way to counting by groups and gives children a chance to practice, but it isn't more efficient than counting by 1s. It is not at the level needed to be considered truly counting by groups to determine how many.

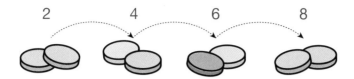

Children arrange the counters in groups of two before counting.

Children who understand this Critical Learning Phase form the groups as they go, using counting by groups as a shortcut for counting by 1s.

■ Knows quantity stays the same when counted by different-sized groups

There is a natural stage when children believe the quantity changes when counted in a different way. If they counted a pile of 32, for example, and were then asked how many there would be if they counted this group by 2s, many young children will assume they will "land" on a different number. The realization that the quantity does not change will come with time and opportunities to notice what happens when counting by groups.

Children who understand this Critical Learning Phase know the quantity stays the same no matter how a group of objects is counted.

USING SYMBOLS

There is no meaning inherent in symbols. Symbols always stand for something else. The meaning a symbol has for a child depends on what the child knows and understands about the concepts the symbol represents.

■ Uses numerals to describe quantities

It is possible for children to know the names of numerals without having any idea about what quantities they represent. What children need to know, however, is not simply how to name the numerals, but also how to use the symbols to represent quantities. Therefore, numerals should be taught in association with what they represent.

Children who understand this Critical Learning Phase can label a particular group of objects with the appropriate numeral.

Chapter Two

Understanding Number Relationships

UNDERSTANDING NUMBER RELATIONSHIPS

C hildren who understand the concepts of more and less understand the relative size of numbers, and the particular differences between them. They know more than how to circle the larger of two numbers, locate the position of a number on a number line, or write < and > signs in the right places on a worksheet. They can compare actual quantities in a variety of settings.

There are two different levels of working with the concept of number relationships: Changing Numbers and Comparing Numbers.

Changing Numbers

When changing one number to another, children begin with a number and then add on counters or take away counters in order to end up with a specified amount. Later, they describe the relationships between these numbers and say, for example, "I had 7, but I wanted 12. I needed to add 5 more." Or, "I had 8, but I wanted 5. I needed to take 3 off."

Comparing Numbers

When comparing numbers, children compare two separate amounts, identifying which is more and which is less and eventually telling how many more or less one number is than the other. For example: "I have 7 cards, but my friend has 12 cards. My friend has 5 more than I do." Or: "There are 8 cars and 5 trucks. There are 3 fewer trucks than cars."

Learning to Change One Number to Another

When children are first learning about numbers, they see each number as distinct from every other number: 6 is 6, and 9 is 9, and that is that. We see evidence of this kind of thinking when we interrupt children in the middle of counting and ask, "How many do you have so far?" It is likely they will not know how many they have counted up to that point. To answer the question, they will have to start over, and count again. For children at this level of thinking, the task of counting is to tell what number they landed on. Since they "haven't landed yet," they do not pay attention to the numbers they are saying as they count.

In order to understand how one number is related to another number, children must move past thinking of each number as a separate entity and recognize that smaller numbers are contained within larger numbers. For example, they need to see that 4 is contained in and is part of 6. Once children see that 4 is a part of 6, they no longer just "label" each counter with a number as they count—they are aware of how many there are as they go. Now, if they are interrupted while they are counting, they can tell how many they have so far, and will be able to continue to count from where they were interrupted.

How Children Learn Number Concepts

The idea of starting with "what we have so far" is at the heart of the "counting on" strategy.

The ability to change one number to another is one of the first indications that children are beginning to move beyond looking at numbers as one and another one and another one. Children demonstrate an understanding that 4 is a part of 6, for example, when they can change a pile of 4 to a pile of 6 by adding 2 more onto the 4. The size of the numbers and the size of the differences between them must also be taken into consideration when determining what children know about number relationships. For example, a child may be able to change a pile of 2 to a pile of 6 and know how many he added on, but not yet be able to tell how many he added when changing a pile of 6 to a pile of 10.

The following Critical Learning Phases identify crucial concepts for children to learn as they develop an understanding of number relationships:

THE CRITICAL LEARNING PHASES

Changing One Number to Another

- Changes a number to a larger number by counting on or adding on a group

- Changes a number to a smaller number by counting back or removing a group

THE CRITICAL LEARNING PHASES (cont.)

Describing the Relationship Between the Numbers

- After changing one number to another, is aware of how many were added or taken away

- Knows how many to add or take away from a number to make another number

CHANGING ONE NUMBER TO ANOTHER

- **Changes a number to a larger number by counting on or adding on a group**

Before children fully understand that a number is a part of another number, some try to change one quantity to another by adding the amount asked for onto the original pile. For example, if a child is asked to change a pile of 4 to a pile of 6, he would count out 6 counters, adding them onto the group of 4 as he counts. When he is finished counting, he thinks that there are 6 counters in the pile — because he landed on 6 when he counted. If he checks to make sure there are 6, he will be surprised! He simply does not take into consideration the 4 that he started with.

Another way young children respond to a request to change one number to another is by making a whole new pile for the second number. This shows that they think of each number as separate from every other number.

How Children Learn Number Concepts

When children figure out they don't need to make a whole new pile, they count the pile they have, starting with one, and then add on counters one at a time until they reach the specified amount. Later, they realize they can start with the number in the original pile and count on by ones.

It is common for children at a certain stage of thinking to try out a number that they think might work and then check their result. For example, if a child is changing 5 to 8, she would add on a "few" counters and then check and see how many there are. Then she would either add on or take away counters and recount until she ends up with the required number.

In time, children learn the specific relationships and can add on the necessary amounts. For example, they will know they can change 4 to 7 by adding 3, and will no longer need to count on to find out.

Children who understand this Critical Learning Phase change a number to a larger number by starting with the original pile and counting on, or adding the correct group of objects.

■ Changes a number to a smaller number by counting back or removing a group

Children move through similar stages when learning to change a larger number to a smaller number. They will often add on to the original pile, even when asked to change a number to a smaller number—without realizing they are making the pile bigger. For example, if a child has 6 and is asked to change the number to 4, she counts 4 items, adding them to the pile as she goes. If you ask her how many are in the pile now, she will say "4," because she just counted to 4. At another stage, she will ignore the pile she started with and make a whole new pile.

Eventually, children recognize that they can make another number by counting from one and removing the "extras." They usually do not pay any attention to how many they took away.

When children recognize that the number they want to end up with is "inside" the number they have, they start with the original pile and count back. They often name each counter as they remove it: "This is the 7, and this is the 6, and this is the 5, so now there are 4 in the pile." Eventually, children will know how many to take away, and change 8 to 4 by taking 4 away.

Children who understand this Critical Learning Phase change a number to a smaller number by starting with the original pile and counting back, or removing the correct group of objects.

DESCRIBING THE RELATIONSHIP BETWEEN THE NUMBERS

■ **After changing one number to another, is aware of how many were added or taken away**

It is important that children eventually notice how many they added on or took away from one number to make a second number. Focusing on the difference between numbers will lead to understanding specific number relationships, like 7 is 3 more than 4.

It is not easy for children to keep track of what they added or took away from a number. At first, they focus on what they ended up with, rather than what they added or took away. So if someone asks, "What did you have to do to change the number?" a child responds with the number that is in the pile. That is, if he changed 4 to 7, he will say something like, "I put

7." This is an indication he is still at the "Count and Land" stage of thinking about numbers, so can't attend to parts of numbers. The amount he adds on disappears into the new total and he doesn't know how many he added on.

After awhile, children are able to figure out this number, sometimes by moving the counters around so they can see what they added. Eventually, they learn to pay attention to what they are doing to change the number, and are then able to tell how many they added on or took off after they have completed the action.

Children who understand this Critical Learning Phase can tell how many they added or took away, without figuring it out, after they have made the change to the number.

■ Knows how many to add or take away from a number to make another number

When children can tell how many they added on or took away without having to stop and figure it out, they are in a position to begin to learn the specific relationships. When they learn these relationships, they will be able to tell ahead of time how many they will need to add or take away.

One of the first relationships children learn is adding or taking away 1. It is noteworthy when a young child changes a number from 4 to 5 by adding 1 without recounting the group of 4. The same is true when a child takes 1 away from 5 to make 4.

Children who understand this Critical Learning Phase know, without counting, the number of counters they need to add to or take away from one number to make another number.

Learning to Compare Numbers

For a child, comparing two separate groups is very different from and more challenging than understanding that one number is contained within another number. To compare two different quantities, children must be able to see what is the same and what is different about these two distinct groups.

There are certain situations where even very young children can compare numbers with ease. For example, when the difference is visually evident, children can easily tell which of two bags has more candy. However, telling how many more one number is than another is a difficult concept for children. At an early stage of thinking, children are not able to interpret the language of "how many more?" They will commonly interpret the question as, "how many in the group with more?" For example, if a child has 5 red cubes and 8 green cubes and is asked, "How many more green cubes than red cubes?" she will commonly reply, "8 more."

Knowing what is meant by the question, "how many more?" is more difficult than we sometimes realize. Its structure makes the question hard to comprehend. A child may actually be able to compare two quantities when asked, "How many 'extra' blue ones are there?" and yet not be able to answer, "How many more?" To complicate matters, "how many more?" is used in different ways. For example, if there is a gathering at the park and someone asks, "How many more children are coming?" the answer can be given without considering the number of children already there. Children may also have heard their parent ask, "How many more times do I have to tell you to pick up your toys?"

How Children Learn Number Concepts

The question, "how many less?" is even more difficult for young children to consider. Thinking about and describing what is not there is harder than thinking about what is there.

It is easier to find the difference between two groups if the groups are organized and lined up. When organized, the differences are visible. It is much more difficult when there are no visual clues and the quantities (expressed in numbers) must be compared. So, if one bag of candy has 14 pieces and the other bag has 5, children can easily tell which bag holds more—but to figure out how many more is much more difficult.

Even after children understand the concepts of more and less, they still need to work with numbers in ways that allow them to internalize the particular relationships between them. The long-range goal is to move past figuring out the relationships to knowing them without counting. The relationships are harder or easier, depending not only on the size of numbers being worked with, but the size of the differences, as well.

The following Critical Learning Phases identify what is crucial for children to learn as they develop a deep understanding of comparing numbers:

Comparing Two Groups: Lined Up

■ Uses what is known about one number to determine another when the groups are lined up

■ Compares two groups that are lined up and determines which is more, and which is less

■ When the groups are lined up, tells how many
more or less, when the difference is 1 or 2

■ When the groups are lined up, tells how many
more or less, when the difference is more than 2

Comparing Two Groups: Not Lined Up

■ Compares two groups that are not lined up and
tells which is more, and which is less

■ When the groups are not lined up, tells how many
more or less, when the difference is 1 or 2

■ When the groups are not lined up, tells how many
more or less, when the difference is more than 2

Using Symbols

■ Uses the greater than (>) and less than (<) symbols as a shortcut for the commonly used words (is
more than, is less than) when comparing objects

COMPARING TWO GROUPS: LINED UP

- ## Uses what is known about one number to determine another when the groups are lined up

When comparing two different groups, children need to see what parts are the same in order to see what is different. As in the following example, one way to determine if a child can see the relationship between two different groups is to ask her to use one connecting cube train to help determine the number of another connecting cube train:

A child counts a red connecting cube train and finds out that it is 8 cubes long. A blue train (11 cubes long) is placed beside the first train. The child is asked if she can use what she knows about the red train to tell how many are in the blue train.

Children who see the two trains as totally separate entities do not realize it is possible to use one train to figure out the other. They have to count the blue train to find out how many cubes it contains. However, children who recognize that the trains are the same up to the point where one sticks out beyond the other, can easily count on to find out the blue train is 11 cubes long. To use what they know about one train to figure out the other, children need to understand and trust that objects that are lined up and matched one-to-one are the same number.

Children who can use a shorter train to figure out the number of a longer train will not be able to use a longer train to determine the number in a shorter train until somewhat later in their development. The concept of less is more difficult for young children to think about, and the concept of counting back is also more challenging.

Children who understand this Critical Learning Phase can line up two connecting cube trains (or other objects lined up and matched one-to-one), and use the number of the first to figure out the number of the second.

■ Compares two groups that are lined up and determines which is more, and which is less

Children find it relatively easy to determine which group is more than another. They can also tell which is "not more," but sometimes take longer to get comfortable using the formal language of "less" or "fewer." Sometimes children use their own language to describe the differences between numbers, for example, "The red cubes have more less," or "The red cubes are littler." Even though the language is not used in a formal way, we can see that the child knows the relationship in question. Teachers can help children learn the language they eventually want them to use by restating what the child said in more formal terms: "Yes, there are less (or fewer) red cubes." It is appropriate to work on developing more formal language only when children understand the concept they are trying to say and describe it with ease, using the language that makes sense to them.

We need to distinguish between an understanding of the relationship and the ability to communicate the concept using correct language. If we were assessing a level of thinking (Ex: can see which group is more and which is less), and not the correct use of vocabulary, we would say the child understands this Critical Learning Phase.

Children who understand this Critical Learning Phase can communicate an understanding of these relationships, informally or formally. For example, they might say, "The red train is longer than the blue train," or "The red train is more than the blue train." Or they might say, "The blue train is littler than the red train," or "The blue train is less (or fewer) than the red train."

■ When the groups are lined up, tells how many more or less, when the difference is 1 or 2

Knowing in a general sense that one number is more or less than another is much easier than identifying how many more or less one number is than another. The easiest difference for children to notice and describe is the one more relationship. Children find it relatively easy to say, "This blue train is one more than that green train." It is somewhat more difficult to describe the difference using numbers, "The 9 train is 1 more than the 8 train." Surprisingly, it is quite a bit harder for children to think about two more. Having the groups lined up helps make the difference easier to see, and somewhat easier to describe.

Children will learn "how many more?" sooner than "how many less?" They may see that one group has less, but there is nothing real to count, so it can be a challenge for them to know what they are describing. It can be easier for children to focus on the amount that is "not there" if they are asked, "What would you have to do if you wanted to make the longer train the same length as the shorter train?"

Children understand this Critical Learning Phase when they can describe the difference between two lined-up groups when the difference is 1 or 2.

■ When the groups are lined up, tells how many more or less, when the difference is more than 2

Asking children to describe differences that are more than 2 is difficult enough that it makes sense to identify it as another stage in learning to compare numbers. A child may appear to know more than he does when comparing two trains that are lined up, because he has learned to report the number of cubes sticking past the other train. He may be able to get the right answer, but if he is focused only on the "part that is sticking out" and not the number of cubes per train, he is not really comparing. One way to help children focus on what is actually happening with the numbers is to have them describe the difference. For example, they might say, "11 is 4 more than 7."

It is more difficult for children to tell how many less—even when the groups are lined up—because they have to tell what is "not there." It is possible to identify whether the child is having difficulty with the language itself, or with the concept of finding the difference, when the language is changed to something easier to understand. For example, "There are 4 white buttons in this row, and 7 black buttons in this row. What would you have to do to make the black buttons the same number as the white buttons?"

Children who understand this Critical Learning Phase can describe the difference between two lined-up groups when the differences are more than 2.

COMPARING TWO GROUPS: NOT LINED UP

The real test of a child's understanding about the difference between numbers is when they compare quantities that are not organized and lined up. This requires the child to think about the number of the two groups they are comparing, because there is no visual comparison, as when objects are lined up. Initially, children will need to actually move and match the objects one-to-one to figure out how many more or less. Eventually, they need to be able to compare two quantities without organizing them.

I counted 8 blue and 11 yellow. I know that 11 is 3 more than 8.

■ Compares two groups that are not lined up and tells which is more, and which is less

Children find it relatively easy to compare two groups and determine which is more and which is less within the range of numbers they can count. They will find it easiest to describe which group is more or less without using any numbers: "There are more green buttons than yellow buttons." They need to be encouraged to tell what they know about the numbers of buttons; for example, "7 is more than 5," or "5 is less than 7."

Children who understand this Critical Learning Phase are able to compare the number of items in two groups of objects, telling which is more and which is less.

- **When the groups are not lined up, tells how many more or less, when the difference is 1 or 2**

  Determining the difference between groups that are not lined up requires children to recognize which parts of the two groups are the same and which are different. If comparing a group of 8 and a group of 12, they need to see that there is a group of 8 within the group of 12, in order to determine how many more are in the group of 12. It is much more difficult to see that 8 is 4 less than 12. Children will often be able to understand this better if they are asked, "What would you have to do to make the 8 the same as the 12?" or "What would you have to do to make the 12 the same as the 8?"

  Children who understand this Critical Learning Phase can describe the difference between two groups by telling how many more one number is than another when the differences are 1 or 2. They will generally be able to tell "how many more" before they are able to tell "how many less."

- **When the groups are not lined up, tells how many more or less, when the difference is more than 2**

  To determine these differences, children will need to move objects for some time before they can figure out the answer without rearranging objects to line them up. Telling how many less continues to be a difficult concept; the teacher will need to model the language used to describe the differences before children will be able to determine this language independently.

How Children Learn Number Concepts

Children who understand this Critical Learning Phase can describe the difference between two groups by telling how many more one number is than another when the differences are more than 2. They will generally be able to tell "how many more" before they are able to tell "how many less."

USING SYMBOLS

The symbols used to show relationships between numbers are not commonly used outside of school so will be unfamiliar to many children. Using symbols is not the most important part of learning number relationships. A child's attention should be focused primarily on number relationships, rather than on the symbolic representation of these relationships.

- **Uses the greater than (>) and less than (<) symbols as a shortcut for the commonly used words (is more than, is less than) when comparing objects**
  Children should first use words to express numerical relationships. They should use natural language (is more than, is less or fewer than). When it becomes easy for them to describe relationships with words, they can then learn to use the greater than (>) and less than (<) symbols as shortcuts for expressing particular relationships.

  Children who understand this Critical Learning Phase can describe number relations with words and with <, and >, and = symbols.

Note: Children are sometimes asked to determine number relationships by using a number line. It is useful to recognize that a number line is a symbolic representation of quantities. When children work with a number line, they are probably not thinking about quantities and relationships—they are using the number line to get to an answer. Even when children are able to find an answer, they typically "count and land."

A number line is helpful only if a child learns something that will aid him in other settings. We cannot assume the child is learning relationships unless he can predict where he is going to land, or can tell how many steps it will take to get to a number he has practiced.

If children use the number line in the same way every time, even after lots of practice, we see it is a tool for getting answers, and not a method for learning relationships. For most children, the relationships between quantities will not be evident when presented on a number line; they will benefit more from comparing groups of real objects.

Chapter Three

Understanding Addition and Subtraction:
Parts of Numbers

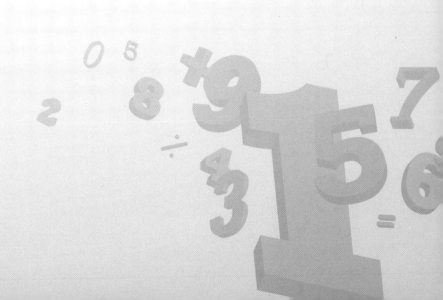

UNDERSTANDING ADDITION AND SUBTRACTION:
Parts of Numbers

L earning basic addition and subtraction facts is essential to children's future success in mathematics. It has long been assumed that children effectively learn basic facts through flash cards and timed tests. However, if knowing basic facts is the foundation for learning more complex computation, children must know more than how to quickly get answers on timed tests. If basic facts are to be foundational, they must be based on an understanding of the composition and decomposition of numbers.

When children know the parts of numbers through 10, they automatically know the basic facts. For example, if a child knows that 8 is made up of 6 and 2, and 5 and 3, and 7 and 1, he also knows: "I have 6 toy cars. I need 2 more to make 8." "I have 5 cookies and you have 8. You have 3 more than I do." "I put 8 cubes in the bag. You took out 1. There are 7 left in the bag." He also knows the relationships expressed as $4 + 4 = 8$, and $5 + 3 = 8$. Eventually, he will see that knowing $3 + 4$ is 7 helps him know that $30 + 40$ is 70, and $23 + 4$ is 27.

Children, who work on learning basic facts though memorizing equations like $3 + 4 = 7$, rather than by learning the parts of numbers, do not usually see how basic facts are related to each other. They tend to think of numbers as one, and one more, and one more, rather than as being composed of parts. They memorize each fact in isolation from the others, so they do not see that knowing $3 + 3 = 6$ can help them know $3 + 4$, or that knowing $5 + 2 = 7$ can help them know $5 + 3 = 8$. They learn $8 - 5 = 3$ as a separate fact from $5 + 3 = 8$.

When a child is asked to find an answer to an addition or subtraction problem she has not memorized, she treats it as a counting problem. She counts to determine "how many" and then writes her answers without paying attention to the particular numbers she ends up with. Practice reinforces the tendency to count, rather than helping children move to the point when they will not need to count. When asked to get answers as quickly as possible, many children simply develop quick counting strategies and thus do not learn any of the equations they don't know.

When determining how to support children in learning basic facts, another factor that must be considered is the common practice of asking them to work with symbols. This is based on the belief that children learn the basic addition and subtraction facts by completing workbook pages, taking timed tests, and using flash cards, drill, and practice computer programs. If children have not learned what they are expected to learn, some would say it is because they haven't had enough drill.

The assumption underlying this approach is that children can learn what a symbol represents by working with the symbol itself. No one believes that learning to read, write, and spell the word chocolate is synonymous with experiencing chocolate. No one believes one can get to know a person by writing that person's name over and over again. But many do believe that knowing how to read and write the symbols $3 + 4 = 7$ is synonymous with understanding the number concepts represented by these symbols. However, there is nothing inherent in a symbol that communicates what it means. Symbols have meaning only when they are associated with the reality they represent.

Here is an opportunity to put yourself in the child's place for a moment. We will use letters of the alphabet to represent numerals, to help you understand what a child experiences when he or she is asked to deal with symbols before a sense of the quantities has been developed. Do not translate these letters into numbers and begin to think, "1, 2, 3," because you will miss the insight into what children experience.

Assume:
a = ■   b = ■■   c = ■■■   d = ■■■■
e = ■■■■■, etc.

What letters belong in the following boxes?
c + e = ☐   b + g = ☐   d + f = ☐

How did you figure out the answers?
Were your fingers useful?

Now that you have figured out those answers,
see how quickly you can tell the answer to the
following:
d + e = ☐

Are you looking for relationships?
Did you notice that d + e had to be a less than
d + f because e is a less than f?
Or did you revert to counting on your fingers?

Try these:

$e + g = \boxed{}$ $d + b = \boxed{}$ $g - c = \boxed{}$ $h - e = \boxed{}$

How fast are you? What would you have to do to get faster? Could you memorize the above facts if you needed to? Would memorizing these facts be of any help in developing a sense of quantity?
Would knowing the answers to addition facts help you in answering the following questions?

How many more is i than c?
Which is more: c + f or b + h?
If you have g people at a party, will s cookies be enough, too many, or just about right? How many will each person get?
About how many grapes could you hold in one hand: h, or m?

Children who deal almost exclusively with symbols begin to feel that the symbols exist in and of themselves, rather than as representations for something else. They do not connect what they know from experience to the symbols they are working with.

The number combinations and relationships children need to understand can only be learned through counting, comparing, composing, and decomposing actual groups of objects. The fact that three and four add up to seven needs to be experienced until the child knows that particular relationship. Just learning to say "3 + 4 = 7" does not guarantee the child really knows the underlying relationships implied in those words.

Contrast learning to say "3 + 4 = 7" presented symbolically, with 3 + 4 shown as a toothpick arrangement.

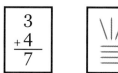

When shown an arrangement, the child can actually see the parts that combine to make a number. There is a distinct difference between these actual quantities and the black marks of symbols. Children need to learn that 3 dots and 4 dots combine to make 7 dots, and then they can learn to write that down using equations that have meaning for them. When children know "by heart" that 3 objects and 4 more objects combine to make 7, they will automatically know the equation 3 + 4 = 7, as long as they associate the abstract symbol with what it represents. The connection in the child's mind between the experience and the symbol is critical, and is the key to developing facility with basic math facts.

Learning Parts of Numbers

Children must know certain foundational mathematical concepts before they can learn the parts of numbers to ten. They must recognize that one number is contained in another number, and they need to be able to see and describe parts of numbers. In other words, they need to "chunk" numbers, rather than think of them as a collection of units. Children must also understand that they will always end up with the same amount when a number is broken apart and recombined in various ways. For example, if you break up 6 into 3 and 3, or 4 and 2, or 1 and 5, you still have 6. These ideas are not as simple as adults sometimes assume.

The following stories are typical of young children learning about numbers and their parts:

Michael made several designs, using 7 tiles for each one. One of his designs had 4 tiles across the top and 3 underneath. His teacher, Mrs. Daniel, looked at Michael's work and commented, "Oh, I see you made a design with 4 and 3." Michael quickly responded. "No, I didn't. I made seven. See, 1, 2, 3, 4, 5, 6, 7," he counted, proving to his teacher he indeed had 7 tiles in his design. For Michael, 7 was one group composed of several single objects. 7 was 7—not 3 and 4.

Ali was working with lima beans that had been painted red on one side. She would count out 5 beans into a paper cup, dump out the beans, and make note of the number of beans that landed with the red side up, and those that landed with the white side up. After recording the number of each color, she would carefully count all the beans to determine the total. Her bewildered teacher thought, "But she put the 5 beans in the cup herself. Why does she need to count them again?" She didn't realize that young children do not yet know which kinds of actions result in changes to the number, and which do not. Ali does not yet trust that it will turn out to be the same number every time.

Mrs. Wu was observing Seth at work. Seth put 6 cubes into a bag, pulled out 3 and immediately said, "So 3 are in the bag." Mrs. Wu said, "You said that really fast. How did you know that so fast?" Seth responded, "Well, you know, every time in Number Talks when you show us 3 dots and 3 more dots, it is always 6. So now I know that 3 and 3 makes 6 all the time!" Mrs. Wu pondered that remark. She had not realized that children might not know that when adding the same two numbers, the sum would always be the same. Mrs. Wu knew that children do not always know they will get the same answer every time they count a group of objects, especially when the counters were spread out and looked different to them. Listening to Seth made her consider that there might be an additional stage of thinking that could be thought of as conservation of combinations.

The children who learn the parts of numbers with relative ease, and apply what they know to addition and subtraction, can do so because they have the foundation for understanding parts, and are building on this foundation. They are able to work with numbers flexibly, taking them apart and putting them back together in a variety of ways. They know that numbers can be combined in any order and that in some cases, organizing and reorganizing numbers can make it easier to add them. They are becoming aware that quantities do not change when broken apart, and that 2 and 4 will yield the same total as 4 and 2. They look for and find relationships so they can use what they know to figure out what they don't know. It is important to be aware of these prerequisite concepts so that children who have not reached this level of thinking are provided the experiences they need in order to ensure success.

The following Critical Learning Phases focus on what is important for children to learn in order to be successful with composition and decomposition of numbers to ten:

THE CRITICAL LEARNING PHASES

Identifying Parts of Numbers

- Recognizes groups of numbers to 5 in a variety of configurations

- Recognizes and describes parts contained in larger numbers

Combining Parts of Numbers

- Describes parts of numbers; counts on to determine total

- Knows the amount is not changed when a number is broken apart and recombined in various ways

- Combines parts by using related combinations including:
  - Doubles plus or minus 1
  - Knowledge of commutative property $(6 + 3 = 3 + 6)$
  - Rearranging parts to create known combinations *(Ex: adding 6 + 4 by moving 1 from the 6 to the 4, making 5 + 5)*
  - Knows totals when combining parts

Decomposing Numbers

- Identifies missing parts by using related combinations including:
  - Using number combinations to solve subtraction $(5 + 3 = 8, so\ 8 - 5 = 3)$
  - Knowing taking away 1 part leaves the other part $(6 - 4 = 2, so\ 6 - 2 = 4)$

- Knows missing parts of numbers to 10

Using Symbols

- Uses equations to record combining and taking away parts

- Interprets equations in terms of combining and taking away parts

IDENTIFYING PARTS OF NUMBERS

It is important for children to recognize that numbers are made up of parts; it requires them to move away from the perception that numbers are a collection of ones.

■ Recognizes groups of numbers to 5 in a variety of configurations

Recognizing small groups of up to 5 objects (referred to as subitizing) is a prerequisite to seeing the parts that make up numbers, and so is the first step in learning basic facts. It stands to reason that children will not be able to see that 7 contains 4 and 3, unless they can recognize the 4 and the 3 when they appear separately.

Children must be able to recognize small groups in a variety of configurations. My own experience as a preschool teacher taught me that it is important not to make assumptions about children's ability to recognize small groups. I had given the children practice in recognizing the arrangements on dot cards, using the same dot arrangements found on dice. Many of my students learned to recognize these arrangements very quickly. However, one day I asked the children to use counters to build what they saw on the cards. To my amazement, I found that many of the children did not use the correct number of counters. Instead, they made an X shape to match the shape of the five dots, and they made a square-ish shape to match the arrangement of the nine dots. I thought I was teaching them the quantities, but they were focused on what the cards looked like. After that, I knew the children must see a variety of number arrangements if they were to focus on the quantity, and not just how the objects were arranged, as in the following for the quantity 4:

Children who understand this Critical Learning Phase can tell the number of various groups of up to 5 objects, without counting.

■ Recognizes and describes parts contained in larger numbers

Once children can recognize small groups when they are arranged in various ways, they need to learn to find these same groups within larger numbers.

When shown arrangements of dots, children will see them in a variety of ways, as described in the following example of 6 dots:

Some might count these dots by ones: "1, 2, 3, 4, 5, 6."

Children who do not yet see parts will see this arrangement as a collection of single dots. This indicates they need prerequisite experiences that will help them learn to see that numbers are made up of parts. They need to learn to change one number to another by adding on or taking off counters, and they need to recognize small groups without counting, before they can see these small groups within a larger number.

A child might see 2 on the top, the 2 outside dots, and 2 on the bottom, and count these dots by twos: "2, 4, 6."

Often, a child counts by twos because he is proud of having learned this skill and wants to show that he can do it. However, even though counting by 2s is a more advanced way of counting, it is still a counting strategy. Children need to see groups of 3 or more before we can be assured they can see the parts of numbers.

It is worth noting that seeing groups of two is sometimes the first indication that children are beginning to move away from seeing the arrangement as composed of single items. Instead of counting by twos, they will often say, "I see 2 and 2 and 2." You can help children begin to see how to combine these 2s if you ask the class, "What do we get when we have 2 and 2?" "How many is 4 and 2?"

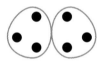

Some children see 3 on one side and 3 on the other side.

Some will see 4 in the middle and 2 on the outside.

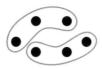

Some will see a line of 3 across the top and another line of 3 across the bottom.

When children look for the parts they know and listen to other children describe what they see, they will understand intuitively that "3 and 3," "2 and 2 and 2," and "4 and 2" are different ways of describing the same thing. This way of looking at numbers can help children when they move to a more formal representation of equalities: 3 + 3 = 4 + 2. Understanding that the same quantity can be described in different ways is also foundational to a later study of algebra, where they will see a more abstract representation of equalities.

It is important to pay attention to what size groups the children can see, because sometimes they only look for one size group, no matter what the arrangement looks like. For example, they may only look for 3s, and get stuck there.

Children who understand this Critical Learning Phase can look at arrangements of dots (or toothpicks, or paper pattern blocks) and identify parts of 3 or more.

COMBINING PARTS OF NUMBERS

After children can see and describe parts, they move through several stages as they learn to combine the parts. They begin by counting all of the dots (or other objects) to find the total. Children often first identify the parts and then count, saying, "I see a 3 and a 4. 1, 2, 3, 4, 5, 6, 7. That makes 7." Other children might count to see what the total is first and then describe the parts.

In time, they develop more and more sophisticated strategies. After sufficient practice, they will know the totals automatically. It is important to recognize that children will learn combinations to 6 or 7 long before they learn the combinations to 10.

■ Describes parts of numbers; counts on to determine total

Counting on is the first step away from counting all, and is important in the child's development of strategies. When counting on, a child might say, "I saw 4 and then I counted 5, 6, 7," or "I knew there were 3 and then I counted the rest, 4, 5." Sometimes they will combine two parts and then count on. "I know 2 and 2 is 4, and then I counted 5, 6, 7."

Children who understand this Critical Learning Phase can see parts of numbers in various arrangements and can count on from the part they know to determine the total.

Note: As important as this stage is, children can get stuck here if their focus is on getting an answer rather than on learning more about numbers and number relationships. When children believe that counting on is the right way to get answers "because the teacher showed them how," they will often stop looking for relationships and stop trying to learn combinations. Many children who get stuck "counting on" are still counting on when they enter middle school. Children need to view counting on as one way to combine parts, but also need to continue to look for other ways that work for them as well.

■ Knows the amount is not changed when a number is broken apart and recombined in various ways

Through the process of describing the parts in a variety of ways, children will begin to notice relationships between the combinations and trust that they still have the same number when they rearrange the parts. For example, they can see that 3 + 3 is 6, but if you move one of the 3 counters, you end up with 2 and 4. They will also see that 2 + 4 and 4 + 2 describe the same amount. Learning the basic facts then becomes a much more manageable task.

Children who understand this Critical Learning Phase can see different ways that numbers can be arranged or described, and trust the total quantity stays the same.

■ Combines parts by using related combinations

When children are given opportunities to look at parts of numbers using materials such as arrangements of dots, toothpicks, or paper pattern blocks, they will notice relationships and can begin to use those relationships to solve problems they don't know. When children notice relationships themselves, they are much more likely to apply this strategy than when the teacher tries to teach them to use it. The teacher provides opportunities for children to look for relationships, and asks them to tell what they noticed. The relationships children notice and use to determine answers include:

■ Doubles plus 1 or minus 1

Children learn doubles relatively early in the process of learning number combinations, with 2 + 2 often being the first combination they know. Once children know doubles and are asked to look for relationships, they will begin to use the strategy of "doubles plus or minus 1" to figure out answers. When children use relationships to figure out the answer, they will say something like, "I know that 4 and 4 makes 8, so 4 and 5 makes 9," or "5 and 5 is 10. So if I take 1 off to make a 4 that would be 9."

■ Knowledge of commutative property (6 + 3 = 3 + 6)

They will see for themselves how the commutative property works. "I know that 6 on the top and 3 more on the bottom is 9. But I can have 3 on the top and 6 on the bottom, and that is 9, too." Seeing how the commutative property works is more effective than just learning these related combinations as "turn-around" facts.

- **Rearranging parts to create known combinations** *(Ex: adding 6 + 4 by moving 1 from the 6 to the 4, making 5 + 5)*

    Sometimes children will create a more familiar combination by reorganizing the numbers, as in the following example: "I wasn't sure what 5 + 3 was, so I moved 1 from the 5, and that makes 4 + 4, and that is 8."

Children who understand these Critical Learning Phases can use what they know about number combinations to solve another related combination.

- **Knows totals when combining parts**

    Eventually, children will just know the basic facts because they have learned the combinations that make up each number to 10. They will say something like, "I just know that 4 and 5 makes 9."

    Sometimes a child will describe 3 or more parts and say, "I know that 3 and 2 and 2 make 7." This is a clue that he did not combine the groups. He most likely counted to find the total, and then described the groups he saw. We can assume this because when people add several addends, they naturally combine two numbers at a time, and add on that total to the next number. They think, "3 and 2 make 5, and 2 more makes 7." When asked to tell what he did, if the child did not need to count, he should be able to say, "I knew that 3 and 2 made 5, and 2 more made 7."

Children who understand this Critical Learning Phase can combine part of numbers without counting.

Range of Numbers

Children first develop proficiency with number composition and decomposition within numbers to 6, then numbers to 10, and then numbers to 20.

Numbers to 6

When children work with numbers to 6, they move from counting all for every combination they are presented with, to counting on, to knowing without counting. They are learning to trust what they know instead of relying on counting. Many children will tend to count even when they don't need to, because they are more confident in their answers when they count. Teachers can help children realize that they do know if they ask questions such as, "Before you count, do you have an idea about what it might be?"

Numbers to 10

By the time children learn parts to 6, they have developed the idea that they don't have to count all the time to be sure they know how many there will be when they combine quantities. It takes longer than most people expect for children to really know the combinations to 10. In part, this is because children often focus on finding an answer, and don't necessarily pay attention to what numbers they combined. When children begin to use relationships, it is more likely that they will pay attention to more than getting an answer. For example, If a child knows 3 + 3 = 6, and they notice that when they change the 3 to a 4, they get 7, they are attending more to the relationships and beginning to build an internal picture of how the combinations they know relate to other combinations they know, and to combinations they don't yet know.

Numbers to 20

Children begin working with numbers to 20 before they know all the combinations to 10. They solve these problems by using the mathematics they know so far. In the beginning, they will primarily solve problems by counting all and counting on. Some will use counting back; some will be able to add 1 or take 1 away without counting.

Once they have facility with doubles, and doubles plus and minus 1 to 10, some children will be able to apply these concepts to numbers to 20. Some will recognize relationships, noticing that 8 + 7 and 7 + 8 have the same answer, and that if 8 + 8 = 16, 16 - 8 must be 8.

When working with numbers larger than ten, developing an understanding of numbers from 10 to 19 as "1 ten and some more" helps children most. For example, when children know that 14 is 1 ten and 4, they will easily solve problems like 14 - 3 by subtracting 3 from 4, rather than by counting back by ones.

DECOMPOSING NUMBERS

As children learn the combinations that make up the numbers to 10, they will reach the point where they know the parts so well, they can identify a missing part when they know the total and one part. This is required if they are to subtract without counting. "If I have 6 cookies and I give you 3, how many do I have?" The child knows the total (6) and one part (3), and has to determine the missing part ("3 plus what equals 6?").

The ability to identify the missing parts of numbers develops more slowly than one might expect. Children need to develop the necessary foundational understandings in order to move forward. That is, they need to have moved past thinking of numbers as a collection of units, and be able to see that small numbers are parts of larger numbers. They also need to be able to combine parts without counting all. And, they need to understand that they will end up with the same amount when a number is broken apart and recombined in various ways.

It takes time for children to reach these levels of understanding. Teachers need to be aware of the complexities of these ideas as exhibited by Charles in the following example:

Mrs. Bracken observed Charles working at an activity using a paper bag and some counters to make subtraction problems. Charles put 7 counters into the bag, pulled out 2, and determined there were 5 left. He peeked in the bag to make sure. He then put the 2 counters back. When he reached in the bag again, he pulled out 5. "Look," he said. "It's sort of the same. Last time I got 2 and there were 5 left. This time I took out 5 and 2 are left."

"That's interesting," Mrs. Bracken commented. She was excited to think that Charles had figured out this important relationship and watched him as he went on to do another problem. This time he pulled 4 out of the bag of 7 counters. He peeked in the bag and figured out there were 3 left. Mrs. Bracken asked, "What do you think would happen if you took 3 out of the bag next time? Do you know how many would be left?" Much to

Mrs. Bracken's dismay, Charles put out his fingers and began to count. He did not yet realize that what he had learned about the relationship of 5 and 2, to 2 and 5, could be applied to other numbers as well.

One of the ways to uncover what a child knows about missing parts is to have her make a pile of a particular number: "Could you make a pile of 6 counters?" After the child counts out the 6 counters, the teacher hides them under her hand and pulls some out. "I am showing you 2. How many are hiding under my hand?"

When young children are first asked to identify missing parts of numbers, they often have no idea how to figure out what they cannot see. Attempting to figure the number out, even if they make errors in the process, is an important first step. Children move through several levels of understanding on their way to knowing the missing parts: from guessing any number, to using their fingers to count all, to counting on or counting back from what they can see.

How a child determines a missing number will depend on what they know about combining parts. A child who knows 3 and 2 is 5 will be able to tell how many are hiding with relatively little practice. But a child who does not know 3 + 2 = 5 will need to figure out how many are hiding, and will probably not remember it the next time they encounter it. Counting is still a primary strategy for children who do not yet know parts.

■ Identifies missing parts by using related combinations

As children move beyond counting, some will use combinations they know to figure out ones they don't know. Number relationships children use include:

■ Using number combinations to solve subtraction (5 + 3 = 8, so 8 − 5 = 3)

Knowing the parts of a number well enough to identify a missing part requires children to combine parts with ease. The more children know about combining numbers, the easier it will be to work with missing parts. Their ability to identify a missing part of a number will lag behind their ability to combine parts. So, if they can combine parts of 7 without counting, they may be working to learn the missing parts of 6, or even 5.

■ Knowing taking away 1 part leaves the other part (6 - 4 = 2, so 6 - 2 = 4)

Children may know or have figured out a missing part, and then use that knowledge in determining a related problem.

Children who understand this Critical Learning Phase can use what they know about combining parts to help them identify the missing part.

■ Knows the missing parts of numbers to 10

Children will reach different levels of proficiency, depending on the size of the number. For example, a child might know the combinations for the smaller numbers, but still count to find out how many when combining larger numbers. It is much more challenging for children to learn all the parts for 7, 8, and 9, than the parts of numbers from 3 to 6. This is partly because there are more combinations to learn, but also because the larger numbers are composed of parts not as easily visualized. The parts of 10 are sometimes learned earlier than parts for smaller numbers (children have lots of experience using their 10 fingers to figure out answers).

Children who understand this Critical Learning Phase know the parts of numbers so well they can identify a missing part almost instantly.

Range of Numbers

Children first develop proficiency for numbers to 6, and then to 10.

Numbers to 6

Children build their understanding of number decomposition by working first with numbers to 6. Once children know with confidence the parts of numbers up to 6, they have learned much about the process of taking numbers apart, and can build on these insights as they begin work with larger numbers.

It is useful for teachers to be aware that some children, particularly kindergarteners, will appear to know parts of 5, but will have just memorized the appropriate pairs in order to identify the missing part. This is evident when the child knows 5, but is completely stumped by 6. We refer to this as "falling off the cliff." If a child is developing an understanding of how numbers work and not just memorizing pairs of numbers, they will know or be able to figure out at least some missing parts of 6.

Numbers to 10

Once children are able to work with numbers to 6 with a certain degree of confidence and facility, they are ready to begin focusing on numbers to 10. Many children are able to figure out missing parts for any numbers from 7 to 10 with relative ease, using counting on—a typical strategy. At this stage, they need to be encouraged to notice and describe parts of numbers and look for relationships among the parts. Then they will rely less and less on counting. Even when children have developed facility for figuring out the hidden or missing parts, we can say they know the particular number combination only when they are able to say the hidden number almost instantly. Teachers cannot assume that children who know the parts of 10 know all the parts of 8 or 9, and sometimes 7.

PROVIDING ENOUGH TIME TO LEARN THE PARTS

Children may work with a particular number in various settings for several months before they know all the parts with ease and confidence. For teachers to recognize the growth that children are experiencing during this period of learning, they must be aware of the stages the children are moving through and how to identify the signs of growth.

At first, the children will not be able to figure out how many are missing or hiding unless they can look at that "missing" part. Sometimes children guess a number that doesn't make sense, even saying a number that is larger than the whole number they are working with. Eventually, they will be able to use their fingers to figure out what is missing. Later, they will be able to count on from what they can see and keep track of how many they counted without using fingers. Ultimately, they move to using what they know to figure out what they don't know. For example, they might say something like, "Last time you were showing me 4, and 2 were hiding. Now you are showing me 2, so 4 must be hiding."

Children learn certain parts before others for any particular number. For example, when using the number 6, they will first learn to identify 1 if they can see a group of 5. Later, they learn that 5 are hiding if they can see 1 counter. Next, they learn the double inherent in 6, knowing if they can see 3, 3 are hiding. 4 and 2 is easier for most children to learn than 2 and 4, and the relationship between them is not immediately apparent. This whole process takes a long time, especially for a 6-year-old child.

Rushing children to memorize the parts can be problematic. Some children will just learn to say number pairs, but will not find this knowledge useful when actually solving problems. Some will try to hide the fact they are counting to get the answer. And some will stop looking for any relationships and just memorize each set of numbers as a separate piece of information. We want children to know the parts of numbers without needing to count. But knowing them because they understand how the numbers work is different from knowing them because they memorized them. When something is memorized, it can be forgotten. If something is understood and learned, it becomes part of what children know about how things work, so it can't be forgotten. Children will be confident in what they know if they see that 3 + 3 = 6, so 3 + 4 is just one more, and it has to be 7.

When children are given the time they need to really learn the parts and the relationships between parts, they will be able to build on this knowledge as they move to larger numbers.

It is worth noting that young children will be able to tell missing parts more easily when they can see some of the counters and know the others counters are "still there" even if they can't see them. It takes longer for them to learn to identify missing parts of numbers if no counters are present. So, for example, they would find the following problem harder: "If you had 6 counters and you gave me 3, how many would you have left?"

USING SYMBOLS

There is no meaning inherent in symbols. Symbols always stand for something else.

The meaning a symbol has for a child depends on what the child knows and understands about the concepts the symbol represents. Symbols become meaningful when they are used to describe numbers and relationships that children know and understand.

How Children Learn Number Concepts

■ Uses equations to record combining and taking away parts

Children should learn to write addition and subtraction equations as ways to describe what they can see in the real world. Children who are working with parts of numbers can write equations to represent what they know and can say. For example, a child might say, "I know there are 2 hiding, because 3 and 2 make 5." They can record this by writing the number sentence "3 and 2 is 5," and later the equation "3 + 2 = 5." Sometimes, they might focus on the number they started with and say, "I put 5 in this bag and I pulled out 3. I know there are 2 left in the bag." They could record this by writing "5 is 3 and 2," and later learn to write "5 = 3 + 2." The key is that the symbols represent a real experience that can be written down.

Children who understand this Critical Learning Phase use equations to record what happens when they combine and separate parts of numbers.

■ Interprets equations in terms of combining and taking away parts

While teaching in my own classroom, I learned that when children work with symbols in isolation from what they represent, they need to deliberately try to think about what the symbols mean in terms of real things. We were reviewing number combinations the children had been working with, using a variety of manipulatives. I held up diverse number arrangement cards that I call "meaningful flash cards:"

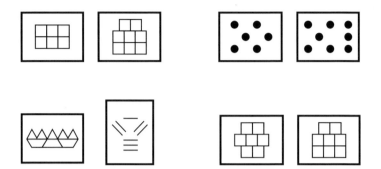

The children were telling "how many" on the cards with ease. After we had worked with several cards, I presented a problem verbally. "Okay, this time I want to know how much is 5 + 3." To my dismay and surprise, all the children in my class put out their fingers and began to count. After they shared their answers, I asked them, "Why do you know the answer when I show you 5 yellow pattern blocks and 3 green pattern blocks, but you count on your fingers when I say the numbers?" One of them explained, "When you say 5 yellow and 3 green, we know what that is, and we know that is 8. But when you say numbers, we just see numbers and we don't know what that is."

"Okay", I said. "This time I will say numbers, but you think of what the numbers mean." "3 + 4," I said. This time they answered quickly. "What did you think about?" I asked. They shared several examples: "I knew 3 toothpicks and 4 more toothpicks make 7 toothpicks". "I knew that if I had 3 cookies and my mom gave me 4 more, I would have 7."

We continued to practice and the fingers did not come out again. I realized that for young children, numbers are adjectives, not nouns. They need to know what the numbers are describing so they won't just picture an equation.

Children who understand this Critical Learning Phase can describe what the numbers might stand for in an equation, and use what they know about parts of numbers to arrive at the answer.

Chapter Four

Understanding Place Value:

Tens and Ones

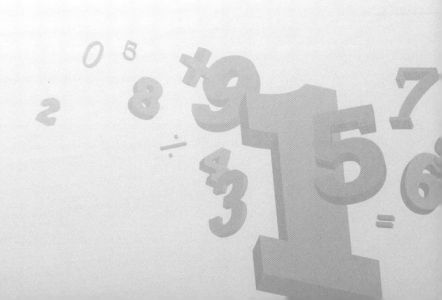

UNDERSTANDING PLACE VALUE: Tens and Ones

Educators use the term "place value" to refer to a range of concepts related to the base ten number system. A central concept is that the value of each digit in a number depends on its position in that number. The focus for children is on labeling each of the places. Another basic idea is that numbers are based on powers of 10; that is, the value of each place is 10 times the value of the digit to the right. The focus is on learning that 10 ones equals 1 ten, 10 tens equals 1 hundred, 10 hundreds equals 1 thousand, and so on. Place value lessons often include rounding, expanded notation, and lining up numbers so children will make sure they are adding tens to tens and hundreds to hundreds. Children learn to read and write large numbers, being careful to place the commas where they belong.

However, if place value concepts are to be meaningful, children need to know more than what digit is in the tens place and what digit is in the ones place. They need to know that the underlying structure of two-digit numbers is based on organizing numbers into groups of tens and ones. This understanding is critical and basic to successful future work with larger numbers and with decimals.

The difficulty young children have understanding place value concepts has not always been recognized. Because children can learn the language of tens and ones with relatively little difficulty, their lack of understanding is often hidden. Teachers are surprised at their children's responses when they ask questions that go beyond naming place values to using these ideas, as shown in the following examples:

Mrs. Huisman's kindergartners marked each day of school by adding a straw to a can labeled "Ones" and, whenever possible, making and placing bundles of tens into a can labeled "Tens." The class was very successful at repeating the right number of tens and ones when requested. One day, she asked the children to tell how many straws were in one of the bundles that they had named a "ten." Much to Mrs. Huisman's surprise, the children offered a variety of guesses: "I think 6." "29!" "There could be . . . 17." For them, the label "ten" was the name of the bundle, rather than the number of straws.

Mrs. Stenberg's class of first graders had been recording the number of days they had been in school each morning since the school year began. On the 57th day, Mrs. Stenberg addressed the class; "Yesterday we had been in school 56 days. Counting today, how many days have we been in school?" The class responded, "57!" "How do we write fifty-seven?" she asked. "Five tens and seven ones," the children said, as Mrs. Stenberg wrote 57. Later that day, Fern's mother brought in 36 cupcakes to celebrate Fern's birthday. Mrs. Stenberg told the class that Fern's mother told her there were 36 cupcakes, and posed a question, "How many groups of ten do you think we could make with these 36 cupcakes?" She was surprised to find that the children had quite a variety of ideas: "I think 6 tens." "8 tens." "I think 4 tens." Mrs. Stenberg reminded them of what they already knew about tens and ones by asking them, "How would we write thirty-six?" Without hesitation, the class chorused, "3 tens and 6 ones." However, saying the number of tens and ones did not lead the children to change their minds about the number of groups of ten they could get with 36 cupcakes. They saw no connection between describing how to write a number and this real-life situation. Mrs. Stenberg was reminded that children often use words correctly without fully understanding the concepts they are referring to.

When the complexity of the ideas inherent in place value concepts are overlooked, and children are deprived of the opportunity to make sense of the work they are asked to do in primary grades, their confusion persists as they move through school. Intermediate and middle school teachers report that place value is still a difficult idea for many of their students. Children's long-term confusion begins when they are asked to work with place value concepts without the prerequisite understandings necessary in order to think of numbers as groups of tens and ones.

There are instructional strategies that can help children develop an understanding of tens and ones. Primarily, they involve organizing quantities into groups of ten and counting those groups. Children reach a deeper level of understanding of ten as a unit if they first work with various smaller groups. Forming and counting smaller groups helps children focus on the processes of grouping and regrouping, make the appropriate generalizations, and provides a foundation for understanding base ten.

The use of manipulative materials, such as connecting cubes, or beans and cups, can help children when learning place value concepts. The unique qualities of connecting cubes can make them especially effective. The children can physically join cubes into a single unit, so that ten single objects become one object. Joining ten cubes into one train does not cause the units to disappear; the children can still count and check to see how many ones they have. This activity is a beautiful model of the idea that the quantity of ten can be one ten and ten ones at the same time. However, even using models does not guarantee that a child will understand the idea the model represents; but it does allow the child the opportunity to make sense of the concept over time.

The models need to represent the idea of tens and ones as clearly and as straightforwardly as possible. The ideas are complicated and should not be made more so by using models that are hard for children to understand. We see the importance of using the right type of model when we consider one of the challenges for children who are just learning place value concepts. Children typically have not fully developed the idea of conservation of number at the time they are introduced to tens and ones. Educators are aware that very young children believe they have "more" if what they are counting is spread out. However, they are not as aware that even as children figure out the number stays the same when objects are spread out, they are still grappling with this concept in other situations. It is not obvious to children which actions result in changing a quantity and which actions do not—even when using models, as we see in the following example:

When Mrs. Hinojos asked her first-graders to organize a bag of peanuts into groups of ten, the children found they had 8 groups of ten with 6 left over. After asking them to tell how many tens and how many ones they had, Mrs. Hinojos asked, "How many is that all together?" She intended to help the children count by tens to determine the total. Before she could begin to model this, several little hands reached for the tubs of ten peanuts and dumped them out so they could "really" count them to find out the actual number. This reminded Mrs. Hinojos of other situations where the children counted one by one. She remembered them counting each straw or pencil on their workbook pages, even when they were pictured in bundles of 10. The children did not trust that they knew how many, unless they counted them one by one.

At a certain stage, children think they will end up with a different number if they count by 2s or 5s. Karl organized a pile of lima beans into 3 groups of ten, with 6 left over. He knew immediately without counting that 3 tens and 6 were 36. When asked how many he thought there would be if he counted them by fives, he thought for a minute and said, "50." His teacher asked him to check and see, so Karl counted them by moving five counters at a time. He counted to 35 and then counted the additional one and said, "There's 36." He didn't seem to notice that was the same number he had arrived at when he grouped the beans into tens and ones.

As surprising as this may be to some of us, thinking that the number changes when you count in a different way is a natural stage in children's development. Karl needs more experiences and time to really trust that the way we count does not affect the outcome.

Another challenge for children as they learn what does and does not make a quantity change is illustrated by Lee Ann's experience with regrouping:

Lee Ann, a second grader, organized her connecting cubes into 3 tens and 4 ones. She was asked to break up one of the tens and put it with the ones and then to tell how many she had all together. Her teacher wanted to emphasize that all she had done was rearrange 3 tens and 4 into 2 tens and 14, so the number had to be the same. Lee Ann's teacher asked her to tell how many there were, now that one ten had been broken up into ones. Much to her teacher's surprise, Lee Ann thought that she now had 44! When her teacher asked her to check and see, Lee Ann was shocked to find she still had 34. She had focused on adding to the ones, but did not realize she had simultaneously taken away from the sets of ten.

When children use materials that model the concept of place value as directly as possible, they can check their thinking. They can see what happens when they count the same number of objects by ones and by fives. Lee Ann was able to check her thinking by counting to see that she still had 34. It will still take time for children to understand what is happening (or not happening) to the numbers, but they can get correct information that challenges them to keep thinking.

How Children Learn Number Concepts

Some math materials used in teaching place value concepts require children to trade ten units for one object (such as a larger block or a colored chip). When children are just beginning to figure out what regrouping is all about, the extra step of trading can cloud their understanding of the concept. The original units are gone, and there is no way for them to verify that they still have what they started with; they simply have to take a teacher's word for it. There is a time when using materials already organized into hundreds and tens, such as base ten blocks, can be helpful. It can be very convenient when dealing with very large numbers; however, such materials should not be used too soon.

Understanding Ten as a Unit

When working with two-digit numbers, children must understand the key idea that groups are counted as single units. Consider this idea in light of children's first and fairly recent counting experiences. Young children have just learned that they must count one and only one item to accurately determine a quantity. They think about quantities for a long time as one, and one more, and one more. When learning about place value, they have to think differently. Now, they have to think of a group of ten as one thing. This requires them to simultaneously hold two ideas—they must think of a group as one unit and as a collection. That is, they must understand that ten is both one ten and ten ones. Before long, they will be asked to think about 1 hundred as a unit, at the same time that it is 10 tens and 100 ones. This level of thinking is very difficult for young children.

In this chapter, we will focus on: 1) the structure of numbers as tens and ones; and 2) adding and subtracting two-digit numbers using the structure of numbers as tens and ones.

Learning the Structure of Two-Digit Numbers

When children are able to organize counters into groups of tens and ones, and use that information to determine the total number without counting, they demonstrate their understanding of the structure of numbers as tens and ones. When they fully understand the structure of number, ideas that were difficult before they understood tens and ones become simple. If they are thinking of ten as a unit, it is as simple to add 2 tens to 5 tens as it is to add 2 to 5.

Developing an understanding of tens and ones, however, is not as clear-cut as we might think. When children are first developing understanding, they may be able to count tens when they are made from connecting cubes, but not when the tens are arranged in piles. They may not be clear about the difference between the number of groups and the total value of the groups, and so may say "40 tens" instead of "4 tens."

Children do not always see the connection between the number of tens and the number of objects. For example, when Olivia was asked to tell how many tens were in the group of 17 she had just counted, she estimated 2.

I observed a class of first and second graders who were working with a set of place value stations. Their activities required them to organize quantities into tens and ones. When I dropped by their classroom, a small group of first graders rushed over to tell me that they had decided to make groups of 7 instead of groups of ten because, "We like 7s better." Another first grader in the class had organized the objects he was working with into 2 groups of ten with 3 leftovers. When counting to see how many all together, he counted the tens correctly, saying "10, 20," but then he went on to count the ones as "30, 40, 50."

These confusions happen because the children aren't making a connection between the numbers we write and the actual structure of the number, and because they aren't clear about when it makes sense to call ten things "one" and when it doesn't.

The following Critical Learning Phases identify the concepts children need to understand if they are to recognize the underlying structure of two-digit numbers as tens and ones:

THE CRITICAL LEARNING PHASES

Understanding Ten as a Unit

■ Counts ten as a single unit

Understanding the Structure of 1 Ten and Some Ones

■ Combines 1 ten and any number of ones up to 9 without counting

- Decomposes numbers from 10 to 19 into 1 ten and some ones

Understanding the Structure of Tens and Ones

- Counts groups of ten

- Knows total instantly when the number of tens and ones is known

- Knows the number of tens that can be made from any group of ones and the number of ones left over

- Knows the number of tens in any two-digit number

- Knows 10 more for any two-digit number

- Knows 10 less for any two-digit number

Using Symbols

- Interprets two-digit written numbers with models of tens and ones

UNDERSTANDING TEN AS A UNIT

■ Counts ten as a single unit

Understanding that ten can be counted as one unit (unitizing) is the major underlying idea that influences everything else children learn about tens and ones. Whether a child understands this concept or not shows up in many different situations, no matter what the task or the size of the number they are working with.

Essentially, there are three ways children's lack of understanding of ten as a unit shows up:

1. Children do not organize into tens.
2. Children count the ones in the ten to determine or confirm the quantity.
3. Children represent 10 with one object.

As we seek to interpret what children are or are not learning, we must always keep in mind the central query: do they understand ten as a single unit?

Children who understand this Critical Learning Phase can think of and count a ten as one thing.

UNDERSTANDING THE STRUCTURE OF 1 TEN AND SOME ONES

Young children commonly think of numbers from 10 to 20 in the same way they think about single-digit numbers. If you were to ask a child to show you 17, he or she would more likely show you one pile of 17 counters than 1 group of ten with 7

---

more. It is not obvious to young children that numerals describe the underlying structure of numbers. At this stage of thinking, the child perceives that the way we write two-digit numbers is how we "spell" them. From the child's point of view, it just happens that we need a 1 and a 5 to write fifteen and a 1 and a 2 to write twelve. Children can even learn to call each digit a "ten" or a "one" and still not really understand that the number is composed of a set of ten and some extras.

■ Combines 1 ten and any number of ones up to 9 without counting

Children show their level of understanding of the structure of numbers to 20 by the way they combine 1 ten and ones. If the child does not consider the ten a unit, they start with 1 and count all the counters to get to the total. At a somewhat higher level of thinking, the child counts on from the ten to arrive at the total. When children count on from ten, they may be thinking of the ten the same as they would any other number, or they may have a beginning understanding of ten being a unit, but do not yet know how many there will be when they add on the ones—so they need to count.

Children who understand this Critical Learning Phase know that numbers from 11 to 19 are composed of a ten and a number of ones, so for example, when they have a ten and 6 ones, they know they have 16.

- ## Decomposes numbers from 10 to 19 into 1 ten and some ones

It is not obvious to some children how many ones there will be when a number like 16 is broken into 1 ten and some ones. These children have learned the pattern for 10 + 6 = 16, without really focusing on what that means. So when they are asked to break a number apart, they are not sure of the number of ones there will be.

If these children are asked how many ones will be left over if they organize the quantity into 1 ten and some ones, some of them will count all of the objects to get to ten, and then count the rest to see how many are left over. We sometimes see children starting with the given number and counting back until they get to ten, keeping track of the number counted.

Children who understand this Critical Learning Phase understand the underlying structure of these numbers; they know that the number itself tells them how many ones will be left over if they break the number apart into 1 ten and some ones.

UNDERSTANDING THE STRUCTURE OF TENS AND ONES

- ### Counts groups of ten

Moving from working with 1 ten to counting and describing groups of more than 1 ten is a big step for many children. Children's lack of understanding of what it means to count groups of ten shows up when they look at 3 groups of ten and 8 ones and say they have 4 groups, or 40. They are confusing the number of groups with the number of tens. Children's confusion between what is and what is not a unit is behind their answer when they say they have 30 groups, rather than 3 groups. These responses are indications that it is not yet clear to them how a ten can be 10 ones and 1 ten at the same time, so they get mixed up between whether they are reporting the number or the value of the groups.

Children who understand this Critical Learning Phase are able to easily distinguish between the questions, "How many groups?" and "How many all together?"

■ Knows total instantly when the number of tens and ones is known

When children organize a number of counters into all the groups of tens they can, we can see evidence of different stages of thinking in the ways they determine the total. Children at one stage of thinking will need to count all the counters to determine what the total is. Children at this level do not see numbers as tens and ones, so grouping them into tens and ones does not help them know how many. Counting by ones is the only strategy they trust for determining the total.

At the next level of thinking, children will be able to count by tens, and then count the ones to determine the total. Children at this level are using a method for counting that requires them to understand how to count by groups and to know the sequence of counting by tens, but they do not yet treat each group of ten as one unit.

How Children Learn Number Concepts

Children who understand this Critical Learning Phase instantly recognize the total for any number of tens plus any number of ones.

Note: It is important to be aware that children may appear to understand the structure of two-digit numbers when they actually do not. Sometimes, children have learned the pattern for determining the total. They know they are supposed to write the number of tens and the number of ones to get the right answer, but don't fully understand that these two digits tell them how many. To find out whether the child understands that 3 tens and 4 is 34, the teacher would have to ask "How many would there be if we counted these by ones?" If the child is not sure, he will most likely need to count by ones to discover the answer.

▪ Knows the number of tens that can be made from any group of ones and the number of ones left over

The reverse of knowing that 3 groups of ten and 4 ones is 34 is knowing that when you have a group of 34 counters, you can make 3 tens. Children who are building an understanding of the structure of numbers will know this at the same time that they know 3 tens and 4 is 34. However, if they have memorized a pattern, or are counting by tens to find the total of 3 tens and 4 ones, they will not know this.

Children who understand this Critical Learning Phase will be able to tell the number of tens they can make when they know the number of objects in a group.

■ Knows the number of tens in any two-digit number

A child needs to be able to identify the number of tens in a given two-digit number whether presented orally or in written form.

Children who understand this Critical Learning Phase will be able to tell the number of tens in any known two-digit number.

■ Knows 10 more for any two-digit number

When children fully understand that numbers are made up of tens and ones, they can add 10 easily because it is just "one" (ten) more.

Some children have learned to combine tens and ones (4 tens and 3 is 43) but not fully understand what that means. Those who don't understand the idea of ten as a unit will think of 10 as a group of ones, and will use their fingers or attempt to count mentally to add 10. They do not see adding 10 as the same as adding 1 ten.

Another way children add 10 more is by thinking of it as a written problem. They go through the same steps they would for any other number they might add, thinking not of the structure of the numbers, but of the steps they learned to use when they add.

Children who understand this Critical Learning Phase can use their understanding of the structure of numbers as tens and ones, so they can easily add one more ten.

■ Knows 10 less for any two-digit number

If children are thinking of ten as 10 ones, they might count to remove 10 objects and then count to see what they have left, or they count back from the total. Some children will take 10 away by using their fingers or attempting to count back mentally, but it is often difficult for them. As was true when adding 10, the ten has no significance for them. Taking 10 away is just like taking away any other number.

Sometimes children can only think about taking 10 away by imagining it is a written problem. They go through the same steps they would for any other number they might subtract, thinking not of the structure of the numbers, but of the steps they learned to subtract.

Children who understand this Critical Learning Phase instantly know what the answer would be when taking one ten away. This indicates that they understand and can use their knowledge of the underlying structure of numbers as tens and ones.

USING SYMBOLS

Our number system uses only ten different numerals that can be put together to write any number—no matter how large or small. This system works because the value of each numeral changes according to the size group it stands for. The size of the group is indicated by the numeral's position in the number.

Children must learn that a particular numeral can stand for many different amounts, depending on its position or place in a number. For children who have just recently learned that 7 stands for a particular number of objects, it is challenging to be asked to understand that 7 also stands for varying amounts, depending on its position. For children who still don't see the difference between 7 and ٢ , or saw and was, and who are still learning to tell their left hands from their right hands, this can be quite a mystery.

This concept is made even more complicated when one number can be represented correctly in several ways but is incorrect if written in slightly different ways. Seventy can be represented as 7 tens and 0 ones or 70, but not as 7 or 07. Seventy-eight can be represented as 78, 70 + 8, 7 tens and 8 ones—even 8 ones and 7 tens—but not as 87 or 708. For many children, these differences are very subtle.

A child's level of thinking regarding ten as a unit can show up when he is asked to interpret symbols. The levels that children most commonly reveal when using symbols are: 1) not organizing objects into tens; and 2) representing 10 with one object.

Teen numbers pose a special problem for children who have been working with numbers to 20 and thinking of them as a collection of ones for a long time before they begin thinking of ten as a unit. A child who has learned to interpret numbers beyond 20 as tens and ones may still have some difficulty thinking of the "1" in teen numbers as a ten; therefore, it cannot be assumed that a child who can interpret numbers to 99 also knows numbers to 19.

Children need to see and interpret numerals written in a variety of ways, such as 4 tens and 3, 40 + 3, or 3 ones and 4 tens, before it can be concluded that they understand how to use symbols to stand for the number of tens and ones.

■ **Interprets two-digit written numbers with models of tens and ones**

When children are asked to use models to show a two-digit number, such as 43, the levels of their thinking can be revealed. If a child thinks of 43 as a group of ones, she will count out 43 objects without showing any awareness of tens. Some children show that they are thinking of 43 as a total of 43 ones by using four connecting cube sticks of ten for the 4 tens—but instead of showing 4 individual sticks, they put them together and then add the ones—and end up with a long train of 43 cubes. When children are not clear about how digits can count groups, they will show 43 as 4 objects and 3 objects, rather than 4 groups of ten and 3 more. It is useful to note that the misconception evident in this situation can be perpetuated if we ask children to count dimes without understanding that the dime represents a group of ten, but a cube does not.

Children who understand this Critical Learning Phase know that numerals describe the underlying structure of numbers as tens and ones, and they can show that 43 means 4 groups of ten and 3 ones.

Learning to Add and Subtract Two-Digit Numbers

When children fully understand that numbers are composed of tens and ones, they can learn to add and subtract two-digit numbers with relative ease, forming additional tens or breaking up tens as needed. However, if children lack this under-standing and view the tens simply as digits in a number, they may learn to get answers—but without understanding.

In order to understand addition and subtraction, children must not only be able to think of two-digit numbers as tens and ones, but also understand how numerals change in value depending on their position, and be able to take numbers apart and put them back together. They ought to be developing an awareness of which actions change the quantities and which do not. Moreover, they need to recognize that adding and subtracting often requires making or breaking up tens and reorganizing the numbers into all the tens possible.

It is easier for children to solve addition and subtraction problems if they know the parts of numbers to 10 so well that they can use them without counting in a variety of settings. For example, a child who wants to add 7 + 6 by making a ten will need to know the parts of 10 (7 + 3) and the parts of 6 (3 + 3).

Note: It will greatly benefit children to know the parts of numbers through 10 before moving on to place value. However, children should advance to working with tens and ones even if they don't know parts of numbers. They can continue to work on learning parts of numbers at the same time they are learning about tens and ones. Their readiness to work with tens and ones will depend on other concepts—not whether or not they know parts of numbers. They need to be able to organize counters into groups of ten and count the number of tens they made.

The following Critical Learning Phases identify the im-portant understandings that must be in place if children are to understand the underlying structure of numbers to 20, and to use this understanding to add and subtract:

How Children Learn Number Concepts

Adding Numbers to 20

- Adds 10 to any number of ones to 9, without counting

- Subtracts 10 from any number from 11-20, without counting

- Adds 2 single-digit numbers with sums larger than ten by reorganizing them into one ten and leftovers

- When adding 2 single-digit numbers that result in a ten and some ones, knows what part of the number is needed to make a ten, and what part will be left over

- After making a ten, adds the ten and leftover ones without counting

Subtracting Numbers to 20

- When subtracting single-digit numbers, knows what part of the number needs to be taken away to get to ten, and what is still left to take away

- Subtracts from numbers to 19 by breaking up the ten when necessary, and knows how many left without counting

Adding Numbers to 100

- Adds multiples of tens to two-digit numbers without counting

- Adds 2 numbers up to 100 by reorganizing them into tens and leftover ones

Subtracting Numbers to 100

- Subtracts multiples of tens from two-digit numbers, without counting

- Subtracts from quantities to 100 by breaking apart tens when necessary, and reorganizing what is left into the remaining tens and leftovers

NUMBERS TO 20

Many children will think about adding and subtracting numbers to 20 in the same way they add numbers to 10. However, if they move to adding and subtracting by making a ten and then adding on or taking away, they will be getting important practice that will help as they begin work with numbers to 100.

ADDING NUMBERS TO 20

- **Adds 10 to any number of ones to 9, without counting**

- **Subtracts 10 from any number from 11-20, without counting**

The difference between adding and subtracting ten, and combining 1 ten and some ones, and decomposing a number into 1 ten and some ones, is subtle. But these subtleties do make a difference to children. The situation and language ask them to think somewhat differently. When combining 1 ten and some ones, the child would likely see a group of ten and a group of ones and "just know" how many there are. When adding a ten to a number of ones, the child needs to think about 10 more than a number. When decomposing a number, the child would be asked to "break it up into a ten and some ones."

Children who understand these Critical Learning Phases can add 10 to any number of ones and know the total without counting, and can decompose any teen number into 1 ten and the correct number of ones.

- **Adds 2 single-digit numbers with sums larger than 10 by reorganizing them into one ten and leftovers**

- **When adding 2 single-digit numbers that result in a ten and some ones, knows what part of the number is needed to make a ten, and what part will be left over**

- **After making a ten, adds the ten and leftover ones without counting**

To determine whether a child can add by making a ten, the teacher can present a problem and ask the following questions:

For example: **6 + 7**

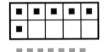

How many of the 7 cubes do you need to add to the 6 to make a ten?

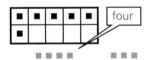

How many will be left over?

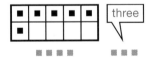

How much is that altogether?

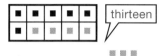

Children who do not yet see that making a ten and some ones automatically reveals the answer to the problem will usually count to find the answer, paying no attention to the ten frame. They ignore the fact that they have reorganized the counters, and go back and count without considering what they just did.

Sometimes, a child has trouble determining the total after making a ten, because he focused on the number he added to the ten and the number left over, and got lost in what he was doing. This is usually because he is not considering the ten as a unit. When children think of the ten as a unit, they know what they have as soon as they determine the number of ones left over after making a ten. They don't have to remember any of the steps they took previously, because the total is obvious to them: it is the ten plus the ones that were left over.

Making a ten and leftovers is much easier for children who know the parts of ten and know the parts of the number being added. Children who do not know the parts will need to count to figure out what they need to add and what will be left. Having to stop and figure this out makes the problem more complex than it has to be.

Children who understand these Critical Learning Phases are able to add 2 single-digit numbers by organizing them into one ten and some ones without counting.

SUBTRACTING NUMBERS TO 20

- **When subtracting single-digit numbers, knows what part of the number needs to be taken away to get to ten, and what is still left to take away**

- **Subtracts from numbers to 19 by breaking up the ten when necessary, and knows how many left without counting**

Using the concept of tens and ones can make addition easier for children, but it is especially helpful with subtraction. Children often solve problems, like 16 – 4, by counting backwards—but this can be problematic. The backward counting sequence is not as easy to use as the forward counting sequence. In addition, children have a hard time figuring out whether or not to count the number they started with, and often end up with wrong answers.

Children who understand tens and ones, and know parts of numbers, solve problems with fewer errors.

For example, consider how children can use tens and ones to solve the problem 15 – 7:

Children sometimes break up the number they are to take away—in this case, the number 7. They take one part of the number from the ones and the other part from the ten. They may think, "I can break the 7 into 5 and 2. I can take the 5 away from the 5 ones in 15, and the 2 away from the 10, and that leaves 8."

Or, the children can take the whole number from the ten and combine what is left with the ones. They may think, "I take 7 away from the 10 and have 3 left. Then I put the 3 with the 5, and that leaves 8."

These same strategies can be used for any problem in which the number being subtracted is larger than the number in the ones place. When children work with these numbers in the ways described above, they are preparing for their subtraction work with two-digit numbers, as well as learning these particular subtraction facts.

Children who understand these Critical Learning Phases can subtract by breaking up teen numbers to make a ten and then breaking up the ten to find the remainder, or by breaking up a ten and adding the remaining ones.

NUMBERS TO 100

Children do not generally obtain the knowledge and logic necessary to solve problems using the structure of numbers as soon as expected in their mathematical development. However, the time spent on learning the composition of numbers to 10, and on developing an understanding of the underlying structure of numbers to 100, will lead to much greater facility with addition and subtraction—rather than to fast counting, poorly remembered facts, and mysterious procedures.

When children are learning to add two-digit numbers, the most important thing is that they make sense, and that their understanding of place value is supported and enhanced by the processes they use. The same mathematical concepts are at play whether children add by combining the ones first and then making all the tens they can (as is traditionally done), or when they add by combining all the tens first. Children who look at the meaning of numbers and use what they know to solve problems know and use more mathematics than they do if they follow a procedure. This is partly because children who learn a procedure do not generally focus on the meaning of what they are doing as much as on the steps they are trying to learn.

It is much easier for young children to understand what they are doing if they: 1) are focused on making all the tens they can, and 2) start with the tens instead of the ones.

ADDING NUMBERS TO 100

Children who are learning to add two-digit numbers need to start with the mathematics they know, and then develop more sophisticated strategies as they learn more about place value and the structure of numbers. Consider the various levels of mathematics children may use when solving the addition problem 38 + 24, using the mathematics they understand, rather than a procedure they do not understand.

When children are asked to solve a problem like 38 + 24 before they understand place value, they can use models or drawings, and count all or count on. Of course, this is very inefficient and time-consuming, but at least it makes sense to the child and creates a need to find more efficient ways. When children are asked to add and subtract two-digit numbers before they understand that numbers are composed of tens and ones, they will necessarily count to get answers. Once they can think of numbers as tens and ones, they can use the structure of the numbers to solve problems more efficiently.

■ Adds multiples of ten to two-digit numbers without counting

Before children fully understand that ten is a unit, there is a stage in their thinking when they solve problems by counting by tens. This makes sense to them, especially when they have models of tens and ones. So, for example, they would add 38 + 24 by saying, "38, 48, 58," and then count on the rest of the ones saying, "58, 59, 60, 61, 62." This is parallel to the young child counting on when working with smaller numbers. It is an important step away from counting all, but children eventually need to move from this strategy to more efficient ones.

When children come to understand ten as a unit, they can add multiples of tens as easily as adding ones. For example, they can add 42 + 30 as easily as they add 4 + 3. They no longer need to count, saying, "40 and 30 is the same as 4 + 3. 4 + 3 is 7, so 40 + 30 is 70. I had 42 so I need to add 2 more on and that makes 72." Some will be able to add without breaking up the 42 into 40 and 2. They would say, "42 + 30 is 72. I just added 3 more tens on to 4 tens I had."

Children who understand this Critical Learning Phase can add multiples of ten without counting.

■ Adds 2 numbers up to 100 by reorganizing them into tens and leftover ones

When children add two numbers, they need to understand that they are trying to make all the tens they can, and see how many ones are left over. In order to make all the tens they can, they need to combine the ones to make a ten, if necessary. This ten is added to the tens they already have. Then they combine all the tens and the left over ones to arrive at the answer.

Children may figure out the number of tens and ones in more than one way, as shown in the following examples:

Example 1
27 + 24

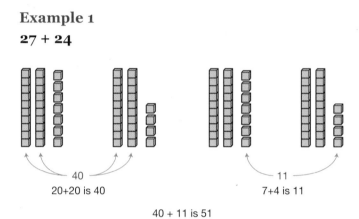

20+20 is 40

11

7+4 is 11

40 + 11 is 51

"20 + 20 is 40
7 + 4 is 11
40 + 11 is 51"

Example 2
27 + 24
"27 + 20 is 47
I need 3 more to make another ten so I get 3 out of the 4 and have 1 left.
Now, I have 50 + 1. That's 51."

Example 3
27 + 24
"20 + 10 is 30
I need to add 3 to the 27 to make 30.
I took the 3 from the 24, that leaves 21.
Now, I have 30 + 21 and that make 51."

How Children Learn Number Concepts

As children become aware of number relationships, they will develop a variety of strategies for adding, based on the numbers they are working with. When they see these relationships, the answer is almost immediately apparent to them. They are not going through steps to see what happens. Essentially, they just see the answer when they see the relationships.

36 + 9
"This is almost like adding 10. I just add the 10 and get 46. Then I take 1 off because it was a 9."

47 + 19
"This is like adding 20. I pretend the 19 is a 20 and then I take 1 off."

26 + 25
"I know 2 quarters is 50 cents. This is like 50 cents but I have an extra penny. So it is 51."

28 + 25
"If I move 2 of the 5 to the 28, that makes 30. I have 23 to add to 30. That's easy. That is 53."

Children who understand this Critical Learning Phase are able to combine two-digit numbers by making all the tens possible, and then combining these tens with the remaining ones.

SUBTRACTING NUMBERS TO 100

Before children understand that numbers are composed of tens and ones, they can count out the required number of objects and solve a problem like 45 – 27, by counting out 45 objects, taking away 27 of those objects, and then counting to see how many are left. As with addition, the fact that these numbers are composed of tens and ones is irrelevant to getting an answer. This is a very cumbersome way to solve problems using numbers of this size, but it does allow the child to make sense of what they are being asked to do.

It is well known that subtraction is harder than addition for children. Adults often overlook one reason two-digit subtraction is not easy for children to understand: it is not obvious to young children whether a change to a number is simply a change in the way it is organized, or if it actually alters the quantity.

Earlier in this chapter, Lee Ann's confusion resulting from reorganizing 3 tens and 4 into 2 tens and 14 was discussed. Her experience was the following:

> Lee Ann believed there would be 44 counters. Lee Ann said, "I added 10 more to the extras so now I have more." After she checked to see how many cubes she had, Lee Ann, along with several other children, was very surprised to find that she still had 34. It appeared that she was not yet able to attend to the fact that when she added ten to the loose cubes, she had simultaneously taken ten away from the groups of ten. Her focus was only on the ten she had added.

When children are still grappling with understanding what is happening to the numbers that are being combined, separated, and reorganized, they need to work with models to check their thinking, and to ponder why the numbers work the way they do.

Children who subtract a two-digit number from another two-digit number often break up the numbers into tens and ones before subtracting. They might think about the following problem in this way:

> **54 − 27 =**
> "54 is 50 and 4.
> I can take 20 from 50 and get 30.
> Now I need to take 7 from 4.
> I don't know how to do that."

What they need to recognize is that they are taking 7 away from 34, not 4. So even if they break up the 54 into 50 and 4, they need to think about how many tens and ones they have left before subtracting 7. If the children use models, they will be able to see that they have 30 and 4 ones left. Teachers can help children focus on this by saying, "How many did you start with?" "So, how many do you still have?" If necessary, teachers can ask, "Did you count the ones you started with?"

■ Subtracts multiples of tens from two-digit numbers without counting

> **56 − 30 =**
> "56 − 30 is 26. I just had to take 3 tens from the 5 tens."

Children who understand ten as a unit can also subtract multiples of tens as easily as subtracting ones. 5 tens minus 3 tens is no harder than 5 – 3.

Practice in subtracting multiples of ten can help children attend to the fact that they have both tens and ones left. The answer to the problem will have to include the ones, requiring them to add on the ones to the remaining tens.

Children who understand this Critical Learning Phase can subtract multiples of ten without counting.

■ Subtracts from quantities to 100 by breaking apart tens when necessary, and reorganizing what is left into the remaining tens and leftovers

As was true for two-digit addition, children need to be able to combine and break apart quantities and reorganize them into tens. Children who understand numbers as tens and ones can solve subtraction problems in more than one way. Consider the mathematics children use to solve the subtraction problem:

45 – 27 =

Some children will take 20 away from 45.

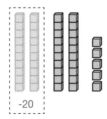

-20

$45 - 20 = 25$

They still have 7 to take away, and can do this in more than one way. Some children will take the 7 in 27 away by first breaking up the 7 into a 5 and a 2. Then they can take the 5 ones from the 5 in 25 and 2 more from one of the tens.

$25 - 7$

7 is 5 and 2

$25 - 5 = 20$

$20 - 2 = 18$

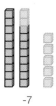

-7

Other children will take the whole 7 away from one of the tens.

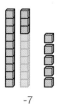

-7

First they break up the 25 into 10 and 10 and 5. They take 7 away from one of the tens, leaving 3. They now have 13 and the 5, which makes 18.

Some children will add up the numbers from 27 to 45 to determine the difference. For example, a child might solve the problem like this:

Adding up
from 27 to 30 is 3
from 30 to 40 is 10
from 40 to 45 is 5
3 + 10 + 5 = 18
45 − 27 = 18

When children find the difference in this way, they need to understand they are determining the number left when they take 27 away. In a sense, they are determining the "missing part" of 45. One way to represent this is to hide 4 tens and 5 ones under a piece of paper and then remove 27 of them so the children can see them. Their job is to figure out how many are under the paper.

So they can think, "I have 27. I need to add 3 more to get to another ten. That would be 30. If I add another ten, that would be 40. I still need 5 more to get to 45. So I think there is 3, and 10, and 5 under the paper. That makes 18."

This same problem could be done on an open number line. The child could start at 27, jump to 30, jump to 40, and jump to 45. However, most children will not see how these jumps relate to a quantity. After they have worked with models and can see what is happening to the numbers, they will be better able to understand what the number line represents.

Children who understand this Critical Learning Phase can subtract two-digit numbers by using the underlying structure of tens and ones.

How Children Learn Number Concepts

Much of what is evident to adults is not easy for children to see. In order to learn the mathematics inherent in two-digit addition and subtraction, children need ongoing and varied experiences, such as focusing on making sense of and thinking about numbers, and on combining numbers and taking them apart in ways that make sense. When children have models to check their thinking, they are able to develop understandings not attained when they are only taught to follow step-by-step procedures without the opportunity to explore, test, and check what is actually happening to the numbers.

Children who understand two-digit addition and subtraction are able to judge the reasonableness of their answers. They can make connections between one type of problem and another, and can use what they know to solve similar problems. They can build on what they have learned and know what is necessary to be successful as they move on to more complex ideas.

How Children Learn Number Concepts

Chapter Five

Understanding Place Value:

Numbers as Hundreds, Tens and Ones with Extensions to Thousands

UNDERSTANDING PLACE VALUE: Numbers as Hundreds, Tens, and Ones with Extensions to Thousands

C hildren's understanding of place value is foundational for the computation they are expected do at their grade level, as well as for the concepts they will learn in later years. It is important that children continue developing an understanding of the structure of the larger numbers they are asked to work with; for example, they need to recognize that 2,345 is composed of 2 groups of one thousand, 3 groups of one hundred, 4 groups of ten, and 5 ones. They should be able to easily reorganize ones into tens (Ex: 42 ones is 4 tens and 2 ones), tens into hundreds (Ex: 17 tens is 1 hundred and 7 tens), and hundreds into thousands (Ex: 15 hundreds is 1 thousand and 5 hundreds). When they understand the structure of large numbers, they will be able to use what they know to add, subtract, multiply and divide with understanding.

They will also be able to build on what they have learned when they begin their work with decimals. When they understand the underlying structure of whole numbers, and are given opportunities to explore the structure of decimals, they will see how the structures are related. For example, they will see that 42 hundredths is worth 4 tenths and 2 hundredths, and will know that .30 is smaller than .5. Developing a deep understanding of the structure of numbers takes time, but is well worth it.

Understanding One Hundred as a Unit

Helping children continue to develop an understanding of place value concepts beyond tens and ones requires that teachers understand the challenges these concepts pose for the learner. Just because children have learned to think about numbers to 100 as groups of tens and ones does not mean they will automatically understand numbers beyond 100. There is another layer of complexity on top of what they learned about tens and ones. When children first learned to think about 10 as 1 unit of ten and 10 ones at the same time, they had to hold these two ideas in mind simultaneously. When they move on to work with hundreds and thousands, they have to hold more than two ideas simultaneously. When working with hundreds, they need to learn to think about 15 tens as 150 ones, as 10 tens with 5 tens left over, and as 1 hundred and 5 tens. They need to be clear about what groups they are describing and what value these groups have in terms of ones.

We know that children who do not yet grasp the full meaning of ten being 1 ten and 10 ones at the same time are sometimes confused when describing 3 groups of ten. They are not always sure whether the correct answer is 30 or 3. Children have similar difficulties when thinking about hundreds, tens, and ones, as we see in the following interaction between Maria and her teacher:

> Maria counted to see how many base ten sticks were on the table in front of her.
> Maria: "There's 15."
> Teacher: "Are there enough tens to make 1 hundred and still have some left over?"

Maria: "Yes."

Teacher: "How many would be left over?"

Maria: "Five."

Teacher: "How much would that be worth all together?"

Maria: "One hundred and five."

Teacher: "Would you check and see?"

Maria counted out 10 tens and lined them up to make 1 hundred. She then counted the remaining tens.

Maria: "Yes, there's 1 hundred and five."

Teacher: (Holding up a ten stick) "How much is this block worth?"

Maria: "Ten."

Teacher: "So how much do you think these blocks are worth?"

Maria: "Oh. 1 hundred and fifteen."

Maria has trouble distinguishing between the number of the groups and the value of the groups. Because describing these numbers in more than one way has never been clear to her, she doesn't realize her answers don't make sense and does not know how to make sense of them by herself.

Children who learn that place value is primarily about the placement of digits do not end up with any sense of the structure of numbers. They may learn to say things like, "10 tens is 1 hundred," and "10 hundreds is 1 thousand," without really understanding what this actually describes.

Judith Sowder's research reveals the lack of understanding that many students have in middle school:

When asked how many $100 bills could be obtained from a bank account with $7200 in it, or how many boxes of 10 golf balls could be packed into a container holding 7200 balls, children almost always do long division, dividing by 100 or 10. They do not read the numbers as 7200 ones or 720 tens, or 72 hundreds, and certainly not as 7.2 thousands.

Therefore, before we begin instruction on decimal numbers, we need to provide more instruction on place value as it is used for whole numbers, by asking such questions as the bank question and the golf-ball question . . . this gives students a flexibility useful with whole numbers, and this flexibility makes it easier to extend instruction to decimal numbers.[1]

Children solve problems like the bank and golf ball questions when they see that the same number can be thought of in different ways. Just as when learning about tens and ones, instructional strategies can help children develop an understanding of hundreds, tens, and ones, and eventually, thousands. They primarily involve organizing quantities into groups, counting those groups, and determining their value. In order to understand that a number can be described in more than one way, children need to physically reorganize the blocks.

Organizing and reorganizing, and composing and decomposing numbers, using models of hundreds, tens, and ones, along with lots of practice and interactions with the teacher and other students, can help children like Maria learn to sort out the various ways of describing numbers.

[1]Judith Sowder, "Place Value as the Key to Teaching Decimal Operations," *Teaching Children Mathematics*, April 1997, 23.

How Children Learn Number Concepts

When children are developing these concepts, it is important that they do not trade one type of block for another. As the children work with the models, their focus needs to be on identifying the relationships the models reveal, rather than on manipulating the models to get answers. They focus on these relationships when they organize and reorganize various models into hundreds, tens, and ones. So, for example, instead of trading 10 tens for 1 hundred (which can cloud the relationship for some students), they line up the 10 tens into 1 hundred. Instead of trading 1 hundred for 10 tens so they can take away 4 tens, they mentally take away or cover up the 4 tens to see that 6 tens are left. When combining 8 and 6, they don't trade 10 ones for a ten, but they mentally or physically put 2 of the ones with the 8 to make another 10 and see that 4 are left. They don't count by tens to see what 14 tens are worth, but they reorganize the tens into 1 hundred and 4 tens to determine that the blocks are worth 140. They need to find out for themselves that 12 tens, 120 ones, 9 tens and 30 ones, and 1 hundred and 20 all describe the same quantity.

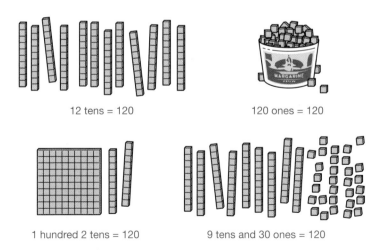

12 tens = 120

120 ones = 120

1 hundred 2 tens = 120

9 tens and 30 ones = 120

Students must spend whatever time it takes for them to learn the important foundational mathematics for developing computational proficiency. Their work with models should lead them to a level of understanding where they can work with these ideas mentally and no longer need the models.

Children who learn the underlying structure of numbers will be able to easily solve the "bank and golf ball" types of questions within the range of numbers they know. They understand how numbers are put together, and as a result, can describe them in many ways.

When children can think of hundreds, tens, and ones flexibly, it is not a big leap to add or subtract. They will see that adding is combining all the tens to see how many hundreds can be made, then how many tens can be made, and how many ones will be left over.

For example: 87 + 45

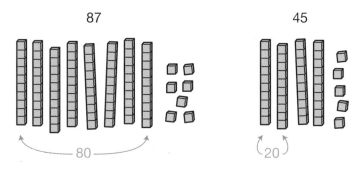

87   45

80 + 20 = 100

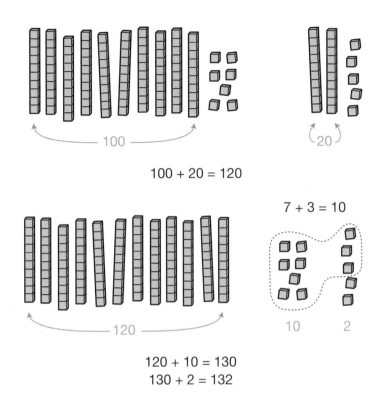

100 + 20 = 120

7 + 3 = 10

120 + 10 = 130
130 + 2 = 132

They see that subtraction is breaking up hundreds and tens as needed, and then reorganizing what is left.

For example: 126 - 38

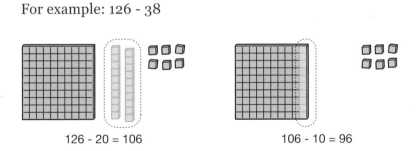

126 - 20 = 106

106 - 10 = 96

"I can take these 2 tens away and I can imagine I took 1 more ten away from the hundred. That means I have 96 left."

$$96 - 6 = 90 \qquad\qquad 90 - 2 = 88$$

"I still have 8 more ones to take away.
I can then take 6 ones away and now I have 90 left.
If I take 2 more away from the 90, I have 88."

Instead of solving every problem in the same way, these children recognize the particular relationships inherent in the numbers they are working with, and arrive at their answers in efficient and logical ways. For example, when adding 198 + 87, many will know that they can move 2 from the 87 to make 200, and immediately see that they have 285. When subtracting 29 from 100, they will almost instantly see that they can subtract 30 from 100 to get 70. Since, they took away 1 too many, they add that one back on to get 71.

When solving the problem 1002 – 426, instead of being confused by the zeros in the number (as so many students are), they could set the 2 aside and take 400 from 1000, leaving 600. They could then use what they know about subtracting from 100 and easily subtract 26 from 600, arriving at 574. They would add the 2 back on to arrive at the answer of 576.

This does not mean that children should have to decide what to do every time they add and subtract. If they are used to thinking about the particular numbers they are adding and subtracting, many will quickly see that adding 98 just requires making 100 and subtracting 2 from whatever is left, or that subtracting 29 is like subtracting 1 less than 30. If they choose to add or subtract this way, it is because they will see the answer

How Children Learn Number Concepts

almost without computing. If the relationships in the number are not obvious, then they can use a predictable and consistent method for computing; usually, that means they start with the largest number, rather than the ones, and reorganize into tens or hundreds as necessary. This is logical to them, and inherently, it is the same mathematics they would use if they started with the ones (Ex: making all the groups they can or breaking up numbers if they need to).

> *Learning to use algorithms for computation with multi-digit numbers is an important part of developing mathematical proficiency. Algorithms are procedures that can be executed in the same way to solve a variety of problems arising from different situations and involving different numbers. Children can and do devise algorithms for carrying out multi-digit arithmetic, using reasoning to justify their inventions and developing confidence in the process.[2]*

Concepts that become obvious to students with practice are not necessarily so when they first begin thinking about what happens to numbers when they add or subtract. When students begin their work with addition and subtraction, most do not use very efficient strategies. Through repeated experiences, questioning by the teacher, and discussions with others, students will come to understand the mathematics and find "easier and easier" ways to solve problems. When children are asked to think about numbers before computing, and are making sense of what they are doing, they develop more understanding of mathematics, as well as confidence in their work.

[2] Jeremy Kilpatrick, Jane Swafford and Bradford Findell, eds: *Adding It Up: Helping Children Learn Mathematics*, (Washington, DC: National Academy Press, 2001), 7.

Learning the Structure of Three-Digit Numbers

It is important that children learn to work with numbers to one thousand with as much ease as they work with tens and ones. The key is learning to think flexibly about numbers, so they can think about 300 as 3 hundreds, as well as 30 tens and 300 ones. They need to learn to work with parts of 1 hundred with as much ease as they work with parts of ten.

The following Critical Learning Phases identify the concepts children need to understand if they are to recognize the underlying structure of three–digit numbers as hundreds, tens, and ones:

THE CRITICAL LEARNING PHASES

Understanding the Structure of Hundreds, Tens, and Ones

- Counts 1 hundred as a single unit

- Knows total instantly when the number of hundreds, tens, and ones is known

- Mentally adds and subtracts 10 and 100 to/from any three-digit number

- Knows the number of hundreds that can be made from any group of tens, and the number of tens left over

- Determines total value of groups of hundreds, tens, and ones by reorganizing them into all possible hundreds, then all possible tens with leftover ones

- Describes any given three-digit number in terms of its value in ones, in tens, and in hundreds

Using Symbols

- Interprets three-digit written numbers with models of hundreds, tens, and ones

- Records the number of hundreds, tens, and ones using appropriate symbolization

UNDERSTANDING THE STRUCTURE OF HUNDREDS, TENS, AND ONES

▪ Counts 1 hundred as a single unit

Understanding that 1 hundred can be counted as one unit is a major step for children who are learning to count groups as units. Because 1 hundred is 100 ones, 10 tens, and 1 hundred, it will take time for children to be able to move flexibly from thinking of 1 hundred as a "big number" to thinking of it as 1 unit, while still knowing it is 10 tens. They need to begin to see that they can think about 4 hundreds, rather than 400 ones.

Children who understand this Critical Learning Phase count groups of hundreds and can report the number of hundreds separately from the total value of a number.

■ Knows total instantly when the number of hundreds, tens, and ones is known

Children who understand the composition of numbers to 1000 as hundreds, tens, and ones instantly recognize the total for any number of hundreds, plus any number of tens, plus any number of ones. The language of hundreds makes it fairly easy for children to describe three-digit numbers. When they see 3 hundreds, they simply have to call it 3 hundreds; if they see 4 tens, they have to know it is 40. So if they saw a model with 3 hundreds, 4 tens, and 6 ones, they would know it was 346.

Children who understand this Critical Learning Phase understand how many there are altogether when they know the number of hundreds, tens, and ones.

■ Mentally adds and subtracts 10 and 100 to/from any three-digit number

When children fully understand that numbers are made up of hundreds, tens and ones, they can add 10 and 100 easily because it is just "one more." Children need to be clear about the number of tens and the number of hundreds, so they will add tens to tens and hundreds to hundreds. For example:

632 + 10 = 642
632 + 100 = 732
632 − 10 = 622
632 − 100 = 532

Children's problems come from a lack of clear understanding of what each digit stands for, and/or thinking of 10 and 100 as collections of ones, instead as 1 unit.

How Children Learn Number Concepts

Children who understand this Critical Learning Phase add multiples of tens and/or hundreds with the same facility as adding ones to ones.

■ Knows the number of hundreds that can be made from any group of tens, and the number of tens left over

Children need to learn more than 10 tens equals 1 hundred. They also need to understand what it means if there are more than 10 tens. For example, they need to understand that 15 tens is 1 hundred and 5 tens, or 100 and 50. When a child is asked, "How many tens?" and has difficulty deciding whether to say 15 tens or 150, he reveals confusion between the number of groups and the value of the groups. This is a key idea that children must grasp in order to understand place value. Students who understand what it means to count groups can simultaneously consider 1 hundred as 1 entity at the same time they consider it as 10 tens and 100 ones. If students are to use these concepts to solve problems, not only must they know the difference between the number of groups and the value of the groups, but they must also be flexible in the use of these ideas, as well as the language used. This flexibility will help them with computation and help build a foundation for later work with decimals.

Children who understand this Critical Learning Phase can tell how many hundreds and leftover tens for any number of tens.

- **Determines total value of groups of hundreds, tens, and ones by reorganizing them into all possible hundreds, then all possible tens with leftover ones**

Children who understand the structure of numbers will be able to reorganize any number of hundreds, tens, and ones and determine the total value with ease.

For example, when calculating the total value of 6 hundreds, 27 tens, and 45 ones:

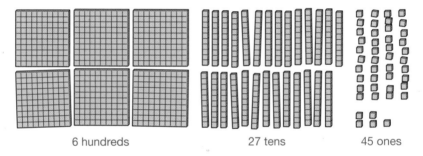

6 hundreds   27 tens   45 ones

they combine 6 hundreds, plus the 2 hundreds (20 tens) taken from the 27 tens, to make 8 hundreds.

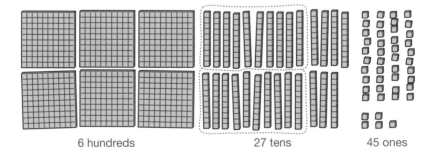

6 hundreds   27 tens   45 ones

         How Children Learn Number Concepts

Now there are 8 hundreds, 7 tens and 45 ones.

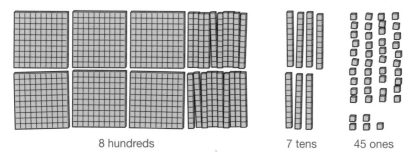

8 hundreds   7 tens   45 ones

7 tens, plus 3 tens (30 ones) taken from the 45 ones, makes another hundred.

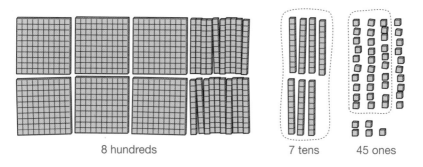

8 hundreds   7 tens   45 ones

Now there are 9 hundreds and 15 ones.

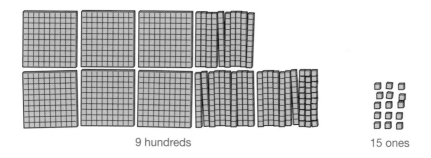

9 hundreds   15 ones

The 15 ones left can be organized into 1 ten, with 5 ones remaining.

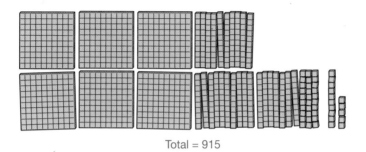

Total = 915

So, 9 hundreds plus the 15 ones is 915.

When children first work with base-ten blocks for three-digit numbers, they will need to actually move and physically reorganize the blocks. They will count out 10 tens and line them up to see that they are the same as the 1 hundred block. Some will check this out by placing a hundred block on top to make sure. They will count the leftover tens to see how many before they know without counting. Some will take 30 blocks from the group of 45 blocks and line them up to make 3 rows of 10.

This kind of task becomes easy for children to do without blocks, if they have reorganized blocks and other models many times until the relationships become apparent. Breaking apart and recombining numbers is something children can make sense of, especially when they have experience in reorganizing to make hundreds and/or tens for themselves. This assumes they are getting the right kind of practice in order to move past simply forming the groups to anticipating what will happen before they actually move the blocks.

Children won't gain from the experiences with models unless they think about what they are doing. Some students get right answers without really focusing on what numbers they are adding or reorganizing; they just line up the blocks and form the groups, and then see what happens. Often, they cannot explain what they added or took away to make the group. To help these students pay attention to what is happening to the numbers as they rearrange and reorganize the models, the teacher and other students will need to ask questions and make observations.

Over time, the students will become more and more proficient. They generally start out needing to count the leftover tens and line up the ones into groups of ten in order to understand what is taking place. Later, they might need to study the blocks, but not actually move them. For example, when they have seen and noted enough times, that 15 tens makes 1 hundred with 5 tens left over, and that 13 tens has 3 tens left over, they will begin to trust that 16 tens will have 6 left over, and will not need the blocks for the next problem.

Children who understand this Critical Learning Phase can mentally organize groups of hundreds, tens (more than 10 tens), and ones (more than 10 ones) to find the total value.

■ Describes any given three-digit number in terms of its value in ones, in tens, and in hundreds

Many of the place value misconceptions children carry forward would be eliminated if they understood not only what the digits in the numbers represent, but also the various ways their values can be described. If the models they use to represent these numbers are made so that the ones, tens, and hundreds are all evident (the hundreds model marked with 10 tens, the tens model with 100 ones, and so forth), they can work with these blocks until the relationships are clear to them.

It is key that the children themselves actually work with, count, reorganize, and analyze—not just observe—the place value models. They can manipulate not only base-ten blocks, but also paper models that allow them to count, circle, and even cut out hundreds, tens, and ones, and determine for themselves the equivalencies between the various amounts.

Children who understand this Critical Learning Phase, know for example, that 340 is 34 tens, 340 ones, and 3 hundreds and 4 tens.

USING SYMBOLS

- **Interprets three-digit written numbers with models of hundreds, tens, and ones**

- **Records the number of hundreds, tens, and ones using appropriate symbolization**

When children have learned to think about numbers in flexible and meaningful ways, they are able to distinguish between various representations of numbers and interpret what they see according to the meaning, rather than by remembering a rule. For example, if they see something written as 300 and 4 and 60, they will not worry that they were not presented "in order." They would read what the numbers say and, if asked to combine them, know to write 364.

I have observed children, trying hard to learn and follow rules, assume the order told the value. These children would write 346, matching the order of the numbers. When children think about what the numbers mean and have learned how to write those numbers down, they will not be confused if they see these ideas shown in various ways. For example, a child could see something like 35 tens, 62 ones, and 4 hundreds, and know they need to record all the hundreds they were able to make, then all the tens, and then all the ones. The order the numbers are presented will not be an issue for them. They would then write the results in the conventional order: 812.

Many of the common errors children make would simply not happen if they had been given the time and experiences they needed to develop place value concepts in meaningful ways. When children are given the required time to learn in a meaningful way, they do not bring misconceptions to new topics in their study of mathematics, and their time spent working with numbers is productive and effective.

Children who understand these Critical Learning Phases understand how the value of a digit is indicated by its place in a number and can interpret and write multi-digit numbers in appropriate ways.

Learning to Add and Subtract Three-Digit Numbers

Adding and subtracting three-digit numbers requires children to use the foundational concepts and understandings described thus far. How they solve the problems they are presented will reveal what they have or have not learned to this point.

When children learn the underlying structure of numbers, rather than one method for getting answers, the mathematical knowledge they have gained results in efficient methods for getting answers. It also provides a foundation for other mathematics—including both decimals and algebra.

The following Critical Learning Phases identify the concepts children need to understand if they are to use place value concepts for addition and subtraction of three-digit numbers:

THE CRITICAL LEARNING PHASES

Adding and Subtracting Three-Digit Numbers

- Adds and subtracts multiples of hundreds without counting

- Knows parts of 1 hundred (in tens) without counting (*Ex: 60 and 40, 70 and 30*)

- Mentally breaks apart 1 hundred into tens and

ones, and recognizes that one of the tens will be broken up *(Ex: 64 and 36)*

■ When adding numbers that result in a hundred and some more, determines what part of the number is needed to make the next hundred and what part will be left over; combines the resulting hundreds, tens, and ones without counting

■ Breaks apart and recombines hundreds, tens, and ones when adding and subtracting

ADDING AND SUBTRACTING THREE-DIGIT NUMBERS

■ **Adds and subtracts multiples of hundreds without counting**

For some children, a step on the way to adding and subtracting multiples is counting up or back by hundreds to determine totals. A child will add 347 + 600 by saying "347, 447, 547, 647, 747, 847, 947." With some experience, children can see that several hundreds can be added at one time—if they are looking at 1 hundred as a unit of 1, instead of as 100 ones.

Children can work with these kinds of problems in ways that make adding hundreds visible. They can start with a model of 347 and add hundreds to this number, as a way to see what happens as they count.

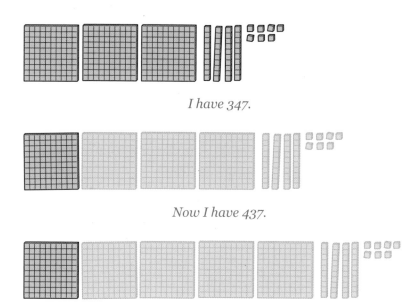

I have 347.

Now I have 437.

Now I have 537.

Adding and subtracting multiples of hundreds without counting is easy when children come to this task with the ability to add numbers to 10 without counting. In other words, if the children know 3 + 6 without counting, they will be able to add 347 + 600 by adding 3 hundreds and 6 hundreds rather than thinking of 300 ones and 600 ones.

Just as when working with numbers to 10, subtracting hundreds is more difficult for children. If children have learned to take parts away from numbers when working with numbers to 10, they will be able to apply it to these larger numbers as well. This means that if a child knows 3 will be left when taking 4 away from 7, because 4 and 3 are parts of 7 (rather than counting back to subtract), this can also be applied to taking 400 away from 700.

How Children Learn Number Concepts

Children who understand this Critical Learning Phase can, for example, add 3 hundreds to 568 as easily as they can add 5 and 3, and can subtract 3 hundreds from 835 as easily as they can subtract 3 from 8.

- **Knows parts of 1 hundred (in tens) without counting** *(Ex: 60 and 40, 70 and 30)*

- **Mentally breaks apart 1 hundred into tens and ones, and recognizes that one of the tens will be broken up** *(Ex: 64 and 36)*

When preparing children to add and subtract, breaking 1 hundred into groups of tens without counting is important. Decomposing 1 hundred builds on what children know about decomposing ten. If they see that ten can be counted as 1 unit, and they know the parts of 10, this will not be very challenging.

What is challenging for some children is breaking 1 hundred into tens and ones. The problem is that they think of the tens and ones separately, so when they break up a ten into ones, they don't consider that they have simultaneously "used up" one of the tens.

> For example: Break up 1 hundred into 2 parts:
> One part is 64. What is the other part?
> A child may think inaccurately about the problem in the following way:
> "100 is 10 tens. I take away 6 tens and that leaves 4 tens.
> I still need to take away 4 ones. If I take 4 away from 10, I have 6 left.
> The answer is 46."

They are off by ten at the end because they don't realize breaking up ten into ones automatically means there is one less ten. They need experiences working with models of tens and ones so they can see for themselves what is happening. Once children understand how this works, breaking numbers up becomes relatively easy, requiring they break up the 10 tens into 2 parts, and then breaking up one of the remaining tens into 2 parts.

The mathematical insight that children will acquire if they work on breaking 100s apart into tens and ones will help them better understand what is going on with numbers when they are adding and subtracting three-digit numbers.

Children who understand these Critical Learning Phases break up 100 into tens and tens into ones without counting, and are aware that they will end up with ten less when they break up one of the tens into ones.

■ When adding numbers that result in a hundred and some more, determines what part of the number is needed to make the next hundred and what part will be left over; combines the resulting hundreds, tens, and ones without counting

When working with two-digit numbers, children learn to reorganize numbers into tens and ones. Working with three-digit numbers requires them to organize numbers into hundreds, tens, and ones.

Three-digit addition is basically combining numbers into all the hundreds possible, then all the tens possible, and then finding out how many ones will be left over.

How Children Learn Number Concepts

The following questions help children focus on this:

> For example: **86 + 38**
> How many do you need to make a 1 hundred?
> If you take that out of the 38, how many will be left?
> So how much is that altogether?

> A child might think about this in this way:
> "If I put 4 on the 86, I will have 90. I just need to add 10 to get to 1 hundred.
> So I need a 4 and a ten. That makes 14.
> I am taking the 14 from the 38 to put it with the 86.
> I can take ten from the 38 and I have 28 left.
> I still need to take 4 more away.
> 28 – 4 is 24.
> I put the 24 with the hundred and that makes 124."

It takes longer to read and write the steps than it does for a child to do the steps. This approach is easy and meaningful if the child knows parts of numbers and takes those parts away without counting, and if the child thinks of addition as making tens and hundreds.

> Another way a child might solve this problem is:
> "I know 80 + 20 is 100.
> But I already have 6, so I need to take 6 out of the 20.
> 20 – 6 is 14.
> I get the 14 from the 38.

38 – 4 is 34
34 – 10 is 24
The answer is 124."

Children who understand this Critical Learning Phase can break up the number they are adding into whatever is needed to make 1 hundred, and as soon as they know how many are left after making 1 hundred, recognize they have 1 hundred and that number.

■ **Breaks apart and recombines hundreds, tens, and ones when adding and subtracting**

No matter what strategies children use to add, they end up finding out how many hundreds, how many tens, and how many ones there are altogether. The following problems illustrate some of the different strategies used:

567 + 259
If they start with the hundreds instead of the ones, they can solve the above problem like this:

"I nccd to make all the hundreds I can.
500 and 200 make 700.
6 tens and 4 tens is another hundred.
I can take 4 tens from the 5 tens.
That makes 800 with 1 ten left.
9 ones and 7 ones is 10 + 6. That makes 16.
16 plus the left over 10 makes 26.
So the answer is 826."

When children are thinking in terms of tens and hundreds, having zeros in the number when subtracting is not an issue for them. For example,

304 – 78

They can solve this problem in the following ways:

"I am going to take the 4 off of 304 and set it aside, because it is easier to subtract from 300. Then I am going to take away the 70 from the 300.
I take it from one of the hundreds so there are 2 hundreds now.
I take 70 from 100. That leaves 30.
So 300 – 70 is 230.
I still have to take the 8 (from the 78) away.
I can take the 8 away from one of the tens. That means I have 2 tens and 2 ones.
So 230 – 8 is 222."
I still have the 4 I took off from the 304, so I put it back on, and that makes 226."

Again, it takes longer to read and write than it does for the child to solve the problem.

Some children will be able to solve this by leaving the 304 whole and not breaking it up into 300 and 4. They know they can take 70 from one of the hundreds without worrying about the 4 ones. So they end up with 200 and 30 and 4.

One way they can subtract the 8 is to break it up into 4 and 4, then take the 4 away and end up with 230. Then they can take the 4 off of 230. If they think of this as taking the 4 from one of the tens in 30, they know the answer has to be 226.

Contrast the level of the mathematics used when a child does it the following way:

304 – 78

"I can't take 8 away from 4. So I need to borrow from the 10.
Oh, there's a zero.
So I need to borrow from the 3.
I cross out the 3 and put a 1 by the zero.
Then I put a 1 by the 4.
Now I have 14 - 8.
I don't remember 14 - 8 so I count up from the 8 to 14.
8, 9, 10, 11, 12, 13, 14.
I used my fingers to keep track.
There are 6.
I write the 6 down and go to the next column.
Oh, I forgot to cross out the zero when I put a 1 by the 4.
I better cross it out and put a 9.
9 – 7. I know that one. It's 2.
I don't have to subtract anything from the 2.
So I bring down the 2.
The answer is 226."

How Children Learn Number Concepts

Even when children are able to follow a procedure and get a right answer, they are not typically thinking of the numbers and what they mean. Children who use the structure of tens and ones are using mathematical thinking and developing the proficiency they need in a world where procedures can be done by machines, and thinking needs to be done by people.

Children who understand this Critical Learning Phase understand the structure of numbers as hundreds, tens, and ones, and use that information to solve problems.

Learning the Structure of Numbers to 10,000 and Beyond

Children who have learned to work with hundreds, tens, and ones have a base of understanding that will serve them well as they begin work with thousands. They will still need practice to become proficient and flexible with these larger numbers, but their previous experiences will help immensely. They will benefit from the use of models that make the structure visible and help show the relationships.

The Critical Learning Phases identified next are the same as those that are important for learning about hundreds, but with thousands added to each one. Children need to understand that 1 thousand is 10 hundreds, 100 tens, and 1000 ones. They need to reorganize numbers into all the thousands they can make, all the hundreds that are possible, and all the tens that are possible, and determine how many ones will be left over.

Children who have a strong foundation with reorganizing hundreds, tens, and ones will have the conceptual underpinnings to work with these numbers, but will need lots of practice to be able to develop the flexibility required to reorganize numbers with ease. They will need to practice with models until they can think about the number of thousands in groups of hundreds, and the number of tens in thousands, and become flexible and confident in their thinking. Working with four-digit numbers means there are more ways to analyze a number in terms of numbers of hundreds, tens, and ones. For most children, becoming flexible and automatic with their ability to describe numbers in various ways will take many experiences.

The following Critical Learning Phases identify the concepts children need to understand if they are to recognize the underlying structure of numbers to ten thousand and beyond:

THE CRITICAL LEARNING PHASES

Understanding the Structure of Thousands, Hundreds, Tens, and Ones

- Counts 1 thousand as a single unit

- Knows total instantly when the number of thousands, hundreds, tens, and ones is known

- Mentally adds and subtracts 10 and 100 to/from any four-digit number

- Knows the number of thousands that can be made from any group of hundreds, and the number of hundreds left over

- Describes any number from 1000 to 10,000 in terms of its value in ones, or tens, or hundreds (3400 is 3 thousands and 4 hundreds, 34 hundreds, 340 tens, and 3400 ones)

- Determines total value of groups of thousands, hundreds, tens, and ones by reorganizing them into all possible thousands, hundreds, and tens with leftover ones

- Interprets four-digit written numbers with models of thousands, hundreds, tens, and ones

Learning to Add and Subtract Numbers to 10,000 and Beyond

Working with 1000s requires an extension of the strategies the children have previously learned. The concept of counting groups should be in place in the child's thinking. At this point, if the children have access to models of 1000, they will easily count thousands as 1. If not, they should go back and work with tens and hundreds before adding these larger numbers. With a strong foundation in understanding hundreds, tens, and ones, and clarity about what each of the digits in a number stands for, the children will be able to add tens to tens, hundreds to hundreds, and thousands to thousands.

The underlying concepts are the same as they are for the smaller numbers, but there are more steps necessary when combining numbers. If we look at adding four-digit numbers, we can see that the problem does not have to be hard if a child has a strong foundation.

For example: Let's see how we can use the structure of thousands, hundreds, tens and ones to solve **2456 + 1087 =**

There are many different ways to add numbers like 2456 and 1087. What seems like a big problem can actually be made quite a bit simpler by looking at the numbers as a whole, rather than as a set of digits.

> One approach is to break 1087 into 1000 and 87. You can then add 2456 and 1000 to end up with 3456.

Now the problem is 3456 + 87.
If you set aside the 3400, the problem becomes
56 + 87.

Adding two digit numbers is something the children have worked on previously. There are many ways this could be solved, as well.

One option is to make a hundred.
87 + 13 is 100. If you take the 13 from the 56,
you end up with 43.
So the answer to 87 + 56 is 143.
Now we combine the 3400 with the 143.
3400 + 100 is 3500.
3500 + 43 is 3543.

Even though there are quite a few steps, the mathematics is not hard if the child can look at 2456 as 2 thousands, 4 hundreds, 5 tens, and 6 ones.

When children have a deep understanding of place value concepts, they will move with confidence into work with thousands.

The following Critical Learning Phases identify the concepts children need to understand if they are to use place value concepts for addition and subtraction of four-digit numbers:

Adding and Subtracting Four-Digit Numbers

- Adds and subtracts multiples of thousands without counting

- Knows parts of 1 thousand (in hundreds) without counting *(Ex: 600 and 400, 700 and 300)*

- Breaks apart 1 thousand into hundreds and tens and recognizes that one of the hundreds will be broken up *(Ex: 640 and 360)*

- When adding numbers that result in a thousand and some more, determines what part of the number is needed to make the next thousand and what part will be left over; combines thousands, hundreds, tens, and ones without counting

- Breaks apart and recombines thousands, hundreds, tens, and ones when adding and subtracting

Children will need to practice adding and subtracting with thousands to develop proficiency. The number of steps can be challenging for some. Others may need to work solely with thousands, or just thousands and hundreds, until it becomes easy. They will need to learn to record steps to make sure they can keep track of their thinking.

For some children, these Critical Learning Phases will grow out of what they have done, and they will work with thousands—and even larger numbers with ease.

Chapter Six

Understanding Multiplication and Division

UNDERSTANDING MULTIPLICATION AND DIVISION

When children move on to learning multiplication and division, they are beginning a study much more complex than learning how to do new operations or more basic facts. Multiplication is not only an important computational skill, it is the foundation for understanding much of the mathematics children will encounter as they move on to higher-level mathematics. Children need to learn more than how to get answers to multiplication and division problems. They also need to develop "multiplicative thinking," because multiplicative relationships underpin many number-related concepts, such as fractions, percentages, ratio and proportion, similarity, functions and graphs, rates of change, and algebra.

Multiplicative Thinking

Educators have not always recognized that multiplicative thinking is a different kind of thinking about numbers than additive thinking. Keith Devlin classifies all thinking about quantities into three categories. He says, " . . . in today's world we are faced with a great many decisions that depend upon an understanding of quantity. Some of them are inherently additive, some multiplicative, and some exponential. The behavior of those three different kinds of arithmetical operations differs dramatically . . ."[1] As this quote makes clear, teachers need to know the difference between additive and multiplicative thinking to ensure that children learn multiplication and division in ways that will support them as they move on to other math concepts.

When teaching multiplication to young children, teachers need to help them begin to recognize some of the differences between multiplication and addition. Central to understanding multiplying is the idea that the two numbers (factors) in a multiplication equation have two different meanings: one number describes how many equal groups there are and the other describes the size of each of the groups. So, in the multiplication equation, 4 x 5, the 4 stands for the number of groups, and the 5 stands for the number of objects in each group.

Another way multiplication differs from addition is that a constant relationship exists between the two numbers. This idea is not usually emphasized in elementary school, yet is basic to understanding the mathematics that builds on multiplication. It means that when one number changes, the other number changes in a predictable way. So, if we know that 2 times 6 equals 12, and we change the 2 into a 3, then we know the 12 changes into an 18. The relationship between the two numbers in a multiplication equation allows us to predict a whole series of numbers. When we know that 1 car has 4 wheels, we also know 2 cars have 8 wheels, and 3 cars have 12 wheels.

Multiplicative thinking also requires children to see the relationship between the factors and apply that knowledge to different situations. The number of wheels on a car is a

[1]Keith Devlin, "Devlin's Angle," *What Exactly is Multiplication?* Mathematical Association of America, http://www.maa.org/, January 2011.

relatively simple example. The following problem is a little less obvious:

> Our class needs 5 leaves each day to feed our 2 silkworms. How many leaves do we need in a week?

> *We know there are 7 days in a week. So, we need to determine how many 7 groups of leaves are. 7 x 5 = 30.*

The next example (more appropriate for middle school students than elementary students) illustrates the usefulness of figuring out the relationship between the numbers and applying it to another related situation:

> Our class needs 5 leaves each day to feed our 2 silkworms.
> How many leaves do we need each day for 12 silkworms?

> *This is no longer a straightforward 7 x 5 problem. We now need to consider the relationship between 5 and 2.*
> *One way to look at this problem is to consider each 2 silkworms a "pair."*
> *So, if 5 leaves are needed for every 2 silk worms, then 10 leaves would be needed for 4 (2 pairs) silkworms, and 15 leaves would be needed by 6 silkworms (3 pairs).*
> *If we had 12 silkworms, we would have "6 pairs."*

So, we would need 6 groups of 5 leaves to feed them. 6 x 5 = 30.

We could also solve it another way:

If 2 silkworms need 5 leaves, then 1 silkworm needs 2½ leaves.
So, 12 silkworms need 12 x 2½.

If children only needed to solve written multiplication problems already set up for them, they would be able to learn to multiply without paying much attention to multiplicative thinking. However, that is not what will make knowledge of multiplication facts useful. Children need to understand multiplicative situations and the language associated with them. For example, they need to understand terms like, "twice as many," "5 times as many," "half as many," "miles per hour," and "dollars per pound."

As explained in research by Constance Kamii and Faye Clark[2], the ideas and language used to express these relationships are not easy for young children to understand. Their research highlights how multiplicative thinking differs from additive thinking and points out children's difficulties in understanding multiplicative ideas.

The researchers showed children three wooden fish: one small, one medium (2 times the size of the first), and one large (3 times the size of the first). The children were told that the middle-sized fish eats "2 times what the first fish eats," and the big fish eats "3 times what the first or little fish eats." They

[2]Faye B. Clark and Constance Kamii, "Identification of Multiplicative Thinking in Children in Grades 1-5," *Journal for Research in Mathematics Education*, January 1996, Vol. 27, Issue 1, 41-51.

asked a series of questions such as, "If the first fish eats 3 pieces of food, how many chips of food would the second fish eat?" The researchers placed 3 chips by the first fish while asking the question. Additive thinkers would generally do one of two things: either add 1 more as the fish grew (3 +1 for the second fish and 4 + 1 for the third fish), or add 2 (for 2 times) and 3 (for 3 times).

The researchers found that 45% of the second graders in the study were able to think multiplicatively, but surprisingly, only 49% of the fifth graders were able to do so with ease. These results suggest that since they were first introduced to multiplication, the fifth graders had not had experiences to support the development of their ability to think multiplicatively.

The following list describes the kind of language and ideas that children need to understand about multiplication by the time they move on to middle school:

Multiplication Situations
Equal Groups (Equivalent Sets)

> *Jackie is going to take cookies to 4 of her friends. She wants to put 6 cookies in each box. How many cookies will she need?*

This is the easiest situation for young children to understand and the focus for much of their work for the first year or more.

Rate/Price/Length

Sheryl likes to walk to the store. She takes about 4 minutes to walk one block. The store is 6 blocks away. How much time will it take her?

These problems require understanding the idea of "per block," "per dollar," and "per foot," and are somewhat difficult for young children to grasp.

Rectangular Arrays

Katja is planning how to set up the room for the parent meeting. There is room for 4 rows of chairs with 6 chairs in each row. How many chairs can fit in the room?

These types of problems require the children to count rows. Children who do not yet think in equal groups see single items rather than rows. Even after they are able to look at the array in terms of rows, they find it very challenging to think of rows and columns at the same time.

Multiplicative Comparison (Scale)

Kathy went to the library to get some books for her classroom. Last week she checked out 4 books. This week she got 6 times as many books. How many books did she get?

This is the same type of problem described in the fish-related example, where comparisons are made using the language of 3 times as much, or twice as long, for example. Children need to be able to think multiplicatively to understand these comparisons.

Combination Problems (Cartesian Product)

Jo Ellen is wrapping presents. She wants each of them to be different than the others. She has 4 kinds of wrapping paper and 6 kinds of ribbon. How many different ways are there for her to wrap the presents?

Combination problems are those that ask for all the possible combinations that can be made, given certain items. For example, how many different outfits can Janelle wear on her trip? She brought a red top, a blue top, a green top, and a black top. She brought one pair of blue jeans, one pair of black pants, and one skirt. Combination problems do not seem the same as other multiplication problems to children learning to multiply, because they don't appear to be made up of groups. In early experiences, they can consider things like making outfits with 3 shirts and 2 pants, using models that help them see what is happening.

Children need to begin working with equal groups situations and spend quite a bit of time working at that level. However, they should eventually be able to work with all the various settings and the language used to describe them.

Relating Multiplication to Division

Division is the inverse of multiplication. This means that generally, the problem asks for either the number of groups (grouping) or the number in each group (sharing), rather than the total number. The following situations show how division relates to the multiplicative situations listed above:

Equal Groups (Equivalent Sets)

> *Jackie is going to take a box of cookies to 4 of her friends. She has 24 cookies. How many cookies can she put in each box?*

Rate/Price/Length

> *Sheryl likes to walk to the store. The store is 6 blocks away. She wants to get there in about 24 minutes. How much time does she have to walk each block?*

Rectangular Arrays

> *Katja is planning how to set up the room for the parent meeting. There is room for 6 chairs in each row. She needs to set up 24 chairs. How many rows does she need?*

Multiplicative Comparison (Scale)

> *Kathy went to the library to get some books for*
> *her classroom. She got 24 books. This is 6 times*
> *as many books as she got last week. How many*
> *books did she get last week?*

Children are not always given experiences that provide them a complete view of multiplication and division. The expectation is commonly focused on memorizing basic facts. However, the central concepts that help children in the long run go far beyond memorizing basic facts. If we are willing to give children the time they need, we can prepare them for the mathematics they will encounter as they move on in school, as well as help them learn basic facts in meaningful ways.

Learning to Multiply and Divide

Children can learn multiplication facts and still not understand what they mean. I learned this the first time I worked with fourth graders. The children were doing a worksheet assigned by their teacher. I stopped by to ask one student to use the counters to show me the problem he was doing, which was 4 x 6. Jake put out 4 counters and 6 counters and then said, "Four times six is twenty-four." "But, I don't see 24 counters," I replied. "That's because this is multiplication," Jake responded.

I have since learned that this kind of response is not unusual. Many children view multiplication as something to memorize, not something to understand. In part, this is

---

because of the emphasis placed on memorizing; but it is also because the concept of thinking of groups as units and then replicating these units is not obvious to children. Many simply don't understand what the teacher is saying when she uses the word "times."

Since the word "times" is not easily understood by young children and interferes with their ability to visualize groups, it is helpful if teachers use language that describes groups (such as "groups of," "rows of," "stacks of," "cups of," or "piles of") instead of always using "times." For example, the teacher would say, "Show me 4 piles of 5," instead of, "Show me 4 times 5."

The kind of thinking required for children to multiply and divide with understanding is different from what they have learned up to this point. Not only do they need to understand groups as units, but children must also be able to keep track of two things at once: the number of groups and the number in each group. They need to be able to hold these two numbers with two different meanings in their mind while they determine the answer to a particular problem.

In order to help children make sense of multiplication, teachers need to focus on the meaning of multiplication by offering them situations (word problems) to interpret, rather than only written equations. Attention should be on the number of groups, not just the size of the groups. They should have children explore multiplication number patterns and look for relationships. And perhaps most important of all, the teacher needs to understand the complexities of multiplication, and be aware of what the child does and does not understand.

The Critical Learning Phases related to multiplication and division are interconnected and often occur simultaneously. However, it is important to be aware of each of them, so particular needs of students can be identified.

The following Critical Learning Phases identify what is crucial for children to learn as they develop a deep understanding of multiplication and division:

THE CRITICAL LEARNING PHASES

Recognizing Equal Groups

- Counts by equal groups (*Ex: skip counts by 2s, 5s, 10s, and so forth*)

- Knows quantity stays the same when counted by different-sized groups (conservation of number)

- Identifies and extends the number patterns that emerge when counting by equal groups

Multiplying Equal Groups

- Counts groups as single entities (unitizes)

- Distinguishes between number of groups and number of objects in each group

- Shows with models "a number of groups of a certain size" when the language of "groups of" is presented with various terms (*Ex: "piles of," "stacks of," "rows of," "cups of," "teams of"*)

- Interprets word problems using models and drawings by showing the number of groups and the number in each group

- Records number of groups in each step of a skip counting pattern, relating it to multiplication

Multiplying Using Rectangular Arrays

- Builds rectangular arrays using "rows of"

- Describes arrays in terms of equal groups (usually by rows)

- Partitions arrays into smaller arrays

- Describes arrays in terms of equal groups when the array is only partially visible

Dividing into Equal Groups

- Divides an amount into equal groups and left-overs using models; tells how many groups and how many in each group

- Using models, interprets the language of sharing and grouping expressed in various ways (Ex: "piles of," "stacks of," "rows of," "cups of," "teams of")

- Interprets "division" situations and creates equal groups (and remainders, if they occur); tells how many groups and how many in each group (and how many left over)

Using Multiplicative Thinking to Solve Single-Digit Multiplication Problems

- Uses multiplication to solve a problem for at least part of the answer and identifies the number of groups (for that part) when explaining the solution including:
  - Multiplying along with counting or adding
  - Doubling groups *(Ex: 2 groups of 4 = 8, 4 groups of 4 = 16)*
  - Using the commutative property *(Ex: 3 x 4 = 4 x 3)*
  - Using the distributive property (breaking up the groups)

Using Multiplicative Thinking to Solve Single-Digit Division Problems

- Divides by trying out a multiplication fact to see if it works, then makes it larger or smaller as necessary

- Uses a known multiplication fact to answer the related division problem

---

Using Symbols

■ Interprets multiplication and division equations

■ Writes multiplication and division equations to describe situations in word problems

Expanding the Language of Multiplication

■ Using models, interprets the language of "twice," "times as many," and "per"

■ Interprets word problems using models and drawings to show "twice," "times as many," and "per"

Preparing for Multi-Digit Multiplication and Division

■ Uses rectangular arrays to show numbers to 100 and beyond; describes the composition of the numbers and determines how many all together

■ Working with numbers to 1000 or more, describes the number of multiples of tens or hundreds in a number (*Ex: finds the number of 20s in a number, the number of 50s, the number of 25s*)

RECOGNIZING EQUAL GROUPS

- **Counts by equal groups** *(Ex: skip counts by 2s, 5s, 10s, and so forth)*

The concept of equal groups is basic to understanding multiplication and division. Children are typically introduced to the concept of equal groups when they learn to skip count. Surprisingly, young children do not always know what "skip counting" means. They think of it as "another way to count" and end up with a fairly common misconception, which is revealed when, for example, they are asked to count a group of objects by 5s and they move one counter at a time as they say the counting sequence. This misconception usually comes about because the children are not actually counting anything when they practice saying the sequence.

Children who understand this Critical Learning Phase count by groups, moving the appropriate number of counters as they count.

- **Knows quantity stays the same when counted by different-sized groups (conservation of number)**

Children are not always able to tell which kinds of actions cause a quantity to change and which do not. There is a natural stage when children think they will land at a different place if they count in different ways. Children cannot be directly taught that the quantity does not change. They need to have experiences that allow them to count and check their thinking, until they recognize and trust that the number will not change.

Children who understand this Critical Learning Phase know that a particular quantity stays the same, no matter how it is counted.

■ Identifies and extends the number patterns that emerge when counting by equal groups

Children need to learn that skip counting produces predictable patterns. When counting wheels on cars, the following pattern emerges: 4, 8, 12, 16, 20, 24... When counting fingers on one hand, the following pattern emerges: 5, 10, 15, 20, 25... Learning to skip count by exploring patterns helps connect the concept to multiplication more clearly than just practicing skip counting patterns without actually counting anything. Children will begin to recognize particular patterns and see that the same patterns come up over and over again, even when counting different things. For example, they will see that the 3, 6, 9, 12 pattern appears when they count sides of a triangle and when they count wheels on a tricycle. Correspondingly, they will see that the 2, 4, 6, 8, 10 pattern appears when counting eyes, ears, and bicycle wheels. Becoming familiar with these patterns is helpful for learning multiplication facts. It is also the foundation for learning multiples of a number.

Children who are not yet able to predict how a pattern is growing will need to count by ones each time in order to add on a group. They are not always aware that the pattern will be the same as another one they experienced.

Children who understand this Critical Learning Phase can determine a number pattern from repeating things that come in groups, and can tell which numbers come next.

MULTIPLYING EQUAL GROUPS

- **Counts groups as single entities (unitizes)**

  In order to understand multiplication, children must recognize that groups can be counted as units. For example, they need to learn to think of a group of six as "1 six," as opposed to "6 ones." The idea of counting groups is central to several Critical Learning Phases. Children come to understand this idea over time as they encounter it in various situations.

  When children begin to work with multiplication concepts, as much focus (or more) should be on forming and counting groups as on finding answers. That means the question, "How many groups?" is as important as, "How many altogether?"

  Children who understand this Critical Learning Phase can respond to the question: "How many groups?"

- **Distinguishes between number of groups and number of objects in each group**

- **Shows with models "a number of groups of a certain size" when the language of "groups of" is presented with various terms** (*Ex: "piles of," "stacks of," "rows of," "cups of," "teams of"*)

- **Interprets word problems using models and drawings by showing the number of groups and the number in each group**

  The three Critical Learning Phases listed here focus on distinguishing between the number of groups and the size of the groups. When children are first asked to show 3 x 5 (or even 3 groups of 5), some have difficulty thinking in groups, and the two numbers are confusing to them. To these children, the meaning of "groups of" is not obvious; they get confused about which number refers to the groups, and which number refers to the number in each group.

For a period of time, children at this stage of thinking should create and count groups, using a variety of models and labels for the groups (Ex: "stacks of," "piles of," "teams of," "rows of") until this language becomes easy to interpret.

When given word problems, the number and size of groups is not given directly. Children have to determine which number tells how many groups, and which number tells how many in each group.

> *Tim has 3 dogs. He gave each dog 2 bones. How many bones did he give his dogs altogether?*

> *5 kids went to the library. They each checked out 3 books. How many books did they check out altogether?*

Children who understand these Critical Learning Phases can respond with confidence to the questions, "How many groups?" and "How many in each group?"

■ Records number of groups in each step of a skip counting pattern, relating it to multiplication

Children's work with skip counting patterns becomes multiplicative when they keep track of the number of groups for each step of the pattern. They would see:

1 ant has 3 body parts (1 group of 3 or 1 x 3),
2 ants have 6 body parts (2 groups of 3 or 2 x 3),
and so on.

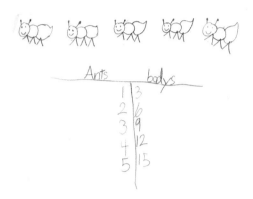

Some children who are recording the pattern for the number of sides of a triangle, while keeping track of the number of groups as they go, will list the addends for each group, indicating they are not thinking multiplicatively.

For example, they would list:
3 + 0 (instead of 1 group of 3)
3 + 3 (instead of 2 groups of 3)
3 + 3 + 3 (instead of 3 groups of 3)

They consider each row of triangles a new problem:
3 + 0 = 3
3 + 3 = 6
3 + 3 + 3 = 9

When asked what they think might come next, they start with 1 and count all sides of all the triangles, instead of seeing that the pattern for sides of a triangle increases by 3 each time.

At another level of thinking, the child is able to count groups, but builds 1 triangle for step 1, 2 triangles for step 2, and 3 triangles for step 3, instead of adding one more triangle for each step of the pattern.

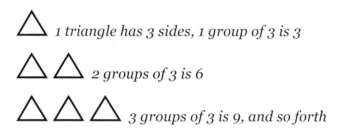

1 triangle has 3 sides, 1 group of 3 is 3

2 groups of 3 is 6

3 groups of 3 is 9, and so forth

At another level of thinking, children can see that the pattern is continuous; growing by 3 at each step, and would add 1 triangle for each new step.

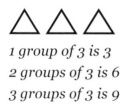

1 group of 3 is 3
2 groups of 3 is 6
3 groups of 3 is 9

Children who understand this Critical Learning Phase can describe the number of groups for each step of a number pattern, and recognize that the pattern grows by one more group each time.

MULTIPLYING USING RECTANGULAR ARRAYS

Rectangular arrays are a particularly useful model for learning about multiplication. However, to many children, the mathematics inherent in arrays is not obvious. Children need many focused experiences with rectangular arrays before they will be able to see the relationships intrinsic to the arrays.

At a certain stage of thinking, children see arrays as a collection of individual units; they do not see the structure of rows and columns. The difficulty children have with arrays is documented by Michael Battista, who describes how children determined the total number of square units in array models. Katy, a second grader, was shown a 7 by 3 rectangle, with the rows and columns indicated only by marks along the edge of the rectangle. She then was shown a plastic square that was the size of the units on the rectangle, and asked to predict how many squares she would need to cover the square completely.

Katy drew squares before making a prediction and counted thirty. For Katy, the row-by-column organization did not exist.

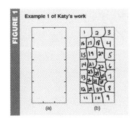

FIGURE 1

Example 1 of Katy's work

(a)   (b)

The same problem was given to above-average students in grades 2–5. Only 19% of second graders, 31% of third graders, 54% of fourth graders, and 78% of fifth graders made correct predictions.[3]

---

[3]Michael T. Battista, "The Importance of Spatial Structuring in Geometric Reasoning," *Teaching Children Mathematics*, National Council of Teachers of Mathematics, November, 1999, 170 – 177.

■ Builds rectangular arrays using "rows of"

When children begin to work with arrays, they need to actually construct the array, focusing on building and describing rows. At first, they will not be inclined to line up the rows to make columns, but instead will form each row separately. Children should practice making rows right along with the other groups they are using: "groups of," "stacks of," and so on.

Children who understand this Critical Learning Phase can build rows, lining them up to make arrays.

For example, the child would build 3 rows of 5, as pictured:

■ Describes arrays in terms of equal groups (usually by rows)

When children begin to think of arrays in terms of numbers of rows, they will be able to look at an array and describe what they see in terms of equal groups, rather than in terms of single units.

There are 4 rows of 5.

Children who understand this Critical Learning Phase can look at an array and recognize and describe it as a number of rows.

■ Partitions arrays into smaller arrays

Children will be able to determine answers to multiplication problems by partitioning an array in smaller sections. When they don't know the multiplication fact shown by the array, they can break up the problem into smaller problems.

So, if a child had an array with 7 rows of 6, she could break it up into 5 rows of 6 and 2 rows of 6 to make it easier to solve.

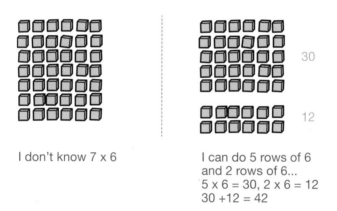

I don't know 7 x 6

I can do 5 rows of 6
and 2 rows of 6...
5 x 6 = 30, 2 x 6 = 12
30 +12 = 42

Children who understand this Critical Learning Phase can describe smaller arrays within a larger array.

- **Describes arrays in terms of equal groups when the array is only partially visible**

  After children have shown they can build and describe arrays where all the squares in the array are visible, they can begin to work with arrays where some or all of the squares are not visible. This requires that they think in terms of equal rows, and do not see each separate square as a unit.

  Children who understand this Critical Learning Phase can describe the rows in an array where the number of rows and the number in each row are marked, but the squares are not illustrated.

DIVIDING INTO EQUAL GROUPS

When we multiply, we know the number of groups and the size of the groups, and need to determine the total. When we divide, we know the total and we need to determine either the number of groups or the size of the groups, depending on the situation. These two types of division are referred to as grouping (measuring) and sharing (partitive).

The grouping process (determining how many groups) is the dividing of a quantity of objects into smaller groups of a particular size to determine the number of groups that can be made.

> For example:
> *We have 15 children in our group. 5 children fit across the rug. How many rows of children can we make?*

Snap together 17 cubes. How many buildings,
4 cubes tall, can you make?

The sharing process (determining how many in each group) is the dividing of a quantity of objects into a particular number of groups to determine the number of objects in each group.

For example:
We have 14 chairs. We need to put them in 2
rows the same length. How many chairs do we
have in each row? Do we have any left over?

Get 19 cubes. Divide those cubes into 3 piles.
How many cubes are in each pile? Any left over?

Children should be introduced to division after they have had many experiences making and counting groups. Many of the Critical Learning Phases necessary to understanding multiplication are also necessary to understanding division. Even though it is the inverse of multiplication, when children are first introduced to division, they see it as an entirely different process. One difference they need to experience is the possibility of some items being left over after equal groups are made. They should work with problems that result in remainders from the beginning of their work with division situations.

Children will be able to build on what they learned previously about counting groups and looking for number patterns in multiplication. Only after they can easily determine the answers to division problems using models will children begin to see how multiplication relates to division.

The following Critical Learning Phases will develop almost simultaneously, but each one needs to be in place for children to understand the process of division:

- **Divides an amount into equal groups and left-overs using models; tells how many groups and how many in each group**

- **Using models, interprets the language of sharing and grouping expressed in various ways** *(Ex: "piles of," "stacks of," "rows of," "cups of," "teams of")*

- **Interprets "division" situations and creates equal groups (and remainders, if they occur); tells how many groups and how many in each group (and how many left over)**
  Children need to experience both kinds of division: sharing and grouping. They do not need to know the names of the processes, but they do need to reach the point where they can easily tell what their answer stands for.

> For example:
> *How many in each group?*
> *We have 20 tiles. If we make 4 stacks, how many tiles will be in each stack?*
>
> The child can describe the answer, "5 tiles."
>
> *How many groups?*
> *We have 20 tiles. How many stacks of 4 can we make?*

The child can describe the answer, "5 stacks."

How many in each group?
Jerry had 15 little cars. He gave them away to
3 friends. They each got the same number of
cars. How many cars did each one get?

The child can describe the answer, "5 cars."

How many groups?
Jerry had 15 little cars. He wanted to give 5
of them to each of his best friends. How many
friends can he give cars to?

The child can describe the answer, "3 friends."

Children who do not quite understand what they are being asked to find out when dividing will not know whether the answer is the number of groups or the size of the groups. They are confused when they see 4 piles of 5, but are supposed to say only one number as the answer. They see 5 and 5 and 5 and 5 and do not understand what is meant by 5 in each group.

Children who understand these Critical Learning Phases can use models to demonstrate the answer to various division problems, describing the answer to show they know it is either the number of items in each group or the number of groups.

USING MULTIPLICATIVE THINKING TO SOLVE SINGLE-DIGIT MULTIPLICATION PROBLEMS

The way children solve multiplication problems reveals something about the level of thinking they have developed. Even when they understand how to set up a model with the correct number of groups and the correct number of objects in each group, it takes a long time for them to truly multiply to get an answer. Children will necessarily use additive thinking strategies to get answers to multiplication problems when they are not yet able to use multiplicative thinking. It is useful for teachers to be aware of the development of these additive strategies and to be able to distinguish them from multiplicative strategies.

In the very beginning, children arrive at their answers by counting. They will then generally move to skip counting, repeated addition, and doubling—all examples of additive thinking. When children count, they do not have to attend to either the number of groups or the number in each group. They simply count all the objects and arrive at their answer.

Skip counting is a more sophisticated way of counting. This strategy requires that the child pay attention to the size of the groups, but not to the number of groups.

Children will sometimes find it easier and more efficient to add the groups instead of thinking about a skip counting sequence. For example, instead of counting by threes they will do the following:

$$3 + 3 = 6$$
$$6 + 3 = 9$$
$$9 + 3 = 12$$

Children use what they know about doubles to find answers. For example, the problem 5 x 8 might be calculated in this way:

8 and 8 is 16.
There are 2 more 8s, so I have to add 16 and 16
to make 32.
There is another 8, if I add 8 to 32, I get 40.

The following Critical Learning Phases indicate the child is moving from additive strategies to multiplicative strategies:

■ Uses multiplication to solve a problem for at least part of the answer and identifies the number of groups (for that part) when explaining the solution

Within multiplication, there is a choice of strategies with varying degrees of sophistication, but each shows some understanding of multiplication including:

▨ Multiplying along with counting or adding
A child may multiply to find out the number for part of the problem, and then count on or add on the rest.

For example:
5 x 6
I know 4 groups of 6 is 24, but there is another row. I can add 6 onto the 24 and that makes 30.

- **Doubling groups** *(Ex: 2 groups of 4 = 8, 4 groups of 4 = 16)*

One way to figure out whether children are using additive thinking or multiplicative thinking is to consider whether or not they are describing the number of groups in their calculation. For example, when asked to figure out the number of squares in an array that was 4 by 8, two third grade children tell how they arrived at their answer. The difference seems subtle, but actually demonstrates two kinds of thinking:

Rick: I figured out 8 + 8, and that was 16. Then I added 8 + 8 again.
Emily: I had 2 8s and that was 16, and 2 more 8s make another 16. That means 4 8s makes 32.

Rick is using repeated addition—additive thinking, while Emily is thinking of each 8 as one unit — using multiplicative thinking.

- **Using the Commutative Property**
(Ex: 3 x 4 = 4 x 3)

Children are using the Commutative Property when they figure out that if 2 groups of 3 are 6, then 3 groups of 2 are also 6. This is not obvious in the model if they are using piles, boxes, or teams. For example, 3 piles of 5 are not physically the same as 5 piles of 3, so it is not immediately obvious to children that the answers can be the same. This relationship

How Children Learn Number Concepts

is clearer when using rectangular arrays, if the child has reached the point where they can use arrays with understanding. For example, using graph paper, the children could cut out all the rectangles with 12 squares they can find. They can then lay them on top of each other to see if any of them are congruent. They would find that 1 x 12 can be placed on top of 12 x 1, 2 x 6 can be placed on 6 x 2, and 3 x 4 can be placed on 4 x 3.

■ Using the Distributive Property (breaking up the groups)

The Distributive Property is employed when a child can break up the number of groups into smaller numbers. For example, a child may not know 6 x 4 but does know 4 x 4 and 2 x 4, so breaks up the 6 groups into 4 groups and 2 groups.

Children who understand these Critical Learning Phases use the numbers of groups as well as the size of the groups, and can use the commutative and distributive properties to get answers to multiplication problems.

USING MULTIPLICATIVE THINKING TO SOLVE SINGLE-DIGIT DIVISION PROBLEMS

Before children are able to use multiplication to find answers for division, they generally use a sharing strategy. Children divide by sharing and counting for a long time before they can see that they can use multiplication to find the answer to a division problem.

> For example:
> Briley has 4 rabbits. She has 12 carrots. How many carrots can she give to each rabbit if she wants them to have the same number of carrots?

Some children will "pass out" the carrots one by one until they run out. Some will realize they can start with 2 carrots and then see what they have left to share.

The following Critical Learning Phases indicate the child is moving from additive strategies to multiplicative strategies:

- **Divides by trying out a multiplication fact to see if it works, then makes it larger or smaller as necessary**

When a child is still learning multiplication facts, he will not know immediately which multiplication fact will help him with a particular division problem. When he tries out a fact he knows to "see if it works," he demonstrates that he knows there is a relationship between these operations.

For example:

45 divided by 9

I don't know what that is. I will try 9 x 3.
That is 27. That's way too small. If I try 9 x 6,
I get 27 plus 27. That's 54. That's too much.
9 x 5 is 2 more 9s. That's 18. 27 and 18 is 45.
That's it. 45 divided by 9 is 5.

Children who understand this Critical Learning Phase are able to select a multiplication fact they know to see if it is the answer to a division problem, and then choose a different one depending on what they found out.

▪ Uses a known multiplication fact to answer the related division problem

At this stage, the child knows the related multiplication fact.

For example:

42 divided by 7

What times 7 is 42?
That's 6 x 7.
42 divided by 7 is 6.

Children who understand this Critical Learning Phase see the relationship between multiplication and division and can use the related multiplication fact to solve a division problem.

USING SYMBOLS

Children need to learn to symbolize multiplication situations, and to associate these symbols with what they represent. This may seem obvious to us, but is not automatic for children. One way to help children make the connection is to have them read the symbols using natural language. For example, they can read 2 x 4 = 8 as "2 groups of 4."

- **Interprets multiplication and division equations**

  The child is able to read an equation and use models to show what it means.

  Children who understand this Critical Learning Phase demonstrate their knowledge of what an equation means by showing the appropriate number and size of groups, using models or drawings.

- **Writes multiplication and division equations to describe situations in word problems**

  Children can listen to a word problem and write the appropriate equation to describe what occurred in the word problem.

  Children who understand this Critical Learning Phase understand what is happening in a word problem and can record it using a multiplication or division equation.

EXPANDING THE LANGUAGE OF MULTIPLICATION

- **Using models, interprets the language of "twice," "times as many," and "per"**

- **Interprets word problems using models and drawings to show "twice," "times as many," and "per"**

Children need experiences that move them beyond thinking of multiplication and division as equal groups only, and expand their understanding of the language to include other multiplicative situations, particularly "times as many," "per dollar," "per mile," "per hour," and so forth.

If children have not reached a certain level of thinking, they cannot understand this type of language. Teachers need to provide experiences for children and model the use of the language, but not ask a child to work with these ideas independently until they see in teacher-led discussions that she appears to understand.

When children understand the use of the language, they should be given experiences that result in an answer that is larger than the known amount, and sometimes, is smaller than the known amount.

> For example:
> Johnny has 4 cookies. Peter has twice as many.
> How many cookies does Peter have?
>
> Johnny has 4 cookies. He has twice as many as
> Peter. How many cookies does Peter have?

Children who understand these Critical Learning Phases can show with models or pictures what "3 times as long," "twice as many," "6 per dollar," or "miles per hour" means. They will be able to determine how many for situations where the answer is bigger than the known quantity, and when the answer is smaller than the known quantity.

PREPARING FOR MULTI-DIGIT MULTIPLICATION AND DIVISION

Children who have reached a level of confidence with single-digit multiplication and division will move on to higher levels of these operations, capable of progress that validates time spent on foundational concepts. While they will still need to work with these larger numbers to see "how it works," make connections to what they already know, and practice to develop facility, they will have the tools and insight to do so.

Children who are asked to work with larger numbers before they have the necessary foundation will take longer, have more misconceptions, and not make the hoped-for progress. Even if they appear successful in learning specific procedures, they will often not be able to apply what they learned to related situations, and forget what they learned once they have moved on to other topics.

A third grade teacher once reported to me that she had spent most of the year working on understanding hundreds, tens, and ones, and on the language and patterns of single-digit multiplication. She realized she had left little time to work on multiplying multi-digit numbers, and that worried her. What she found, however, was that some things that used to be difficult to teach her students were not that year. For example, when she gave her kids the problem 12 x 24, they said, "That's easy. That is just 10 times 24, which is 240, and 2 times 24, which is 48. So that makes it 288."

The children were more successful when she had given them time to build the foundational understandings they needed, than they were when she had spent more time "teaching" them.

Success with higher levels of multiplication and division depends on the ability to count groups as units, and to partition these units into smaller units (5 groups of 6 can be thought of as 3 groups of 6 and 2 groups of 6). Children need to be confident with the use of arrays, and to be able to describe the array in terms of "rows of," and potentially in terms of "columns." Equally important, they need to understand the structure of numbers as hundreds, tens, ones, and beyond.

To develop the understanding of the larger numbers necessary for multi-digit multiplication and division, children need to explore what happens to numbers when they multiply and divide them before they are asked to work with symbolic representations of these numbers.

■ Uses rectangular arrays to show numbers to 100 and beyond; describes the composition of the numbers and determines how many all together

In order to do multi-digit multiplication with understanding, children need to see how large numbers can be shown on arrays and then combined, by looking for parts of the number that can be easily combined.

For example:

Show an array that is 10 rows of 15 (or 10 by 15).

What do you notice? Do you see any parts of the array that you know without counting? How much is 10 rows of 15 altogether?

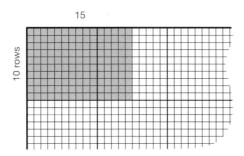

Now show an array that is 12 rows of 15.

What do you notice?

What is the difference between the total of 10 rows of 15 and 12 rows of 15?

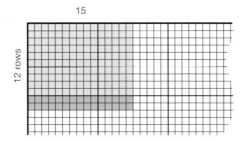

Janie was working on an activity where she was to make an array of 23 times 62. Janie could not picture what that array would look like so she thought about it in this way:

I can do 10 rows of 23.

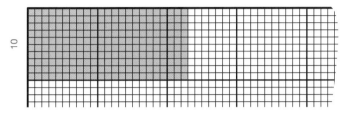

This is 20 rows of 23.

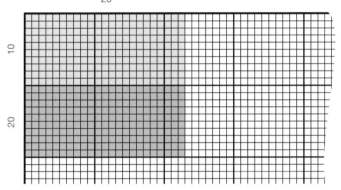

This is 30 rows of 23.

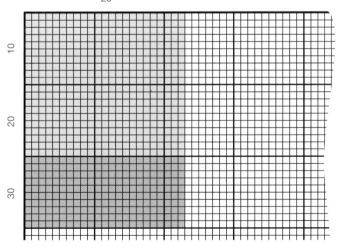

Now I get it. This is 60 rows of 23.

23

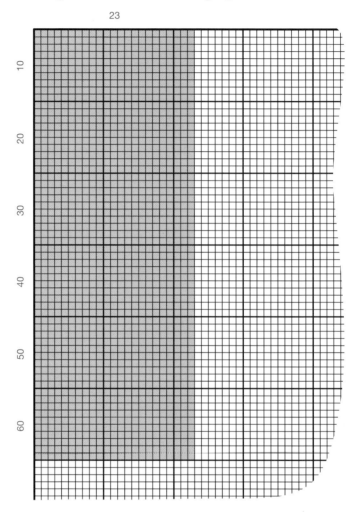

How Children Learn Number Concepts

I need 62 rows, so I need 2 more rows of 23.

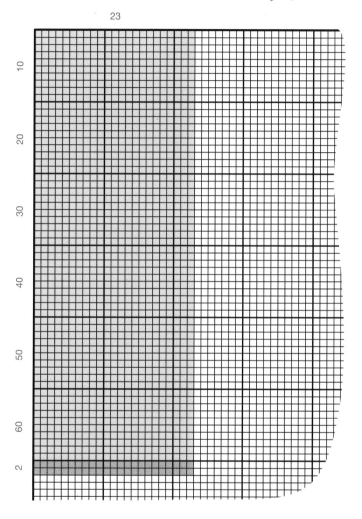

23

When I was making the array, I noticed that 10 rows of 20 made 2 hundreds and 10 rows of 3 make 30. So when I got done, I could see 6 rows of 200 and 6 rows of 30.

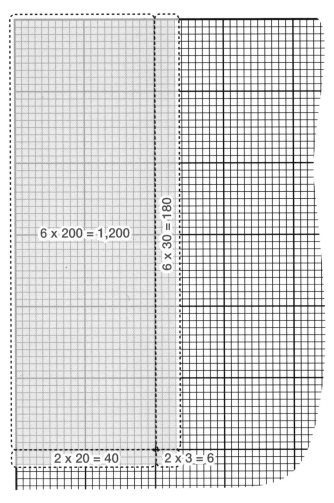

6 x 200 = 1200 and 6 x 30 =180.
1200 + 180 = 1380. I see 2 20s. 2 x 20 = 40.
1380 + 20 = 1400 and 1400 + 20 = 1420.
2 x 3 is left. That's 6. So 1420 + 6 = 1426.

How Children Learn Number Concepts

Children who have not developed an understanding of the structure of numbers will not see "chunks" of numbers, but will need to count. They will not be able to easily look at a number in more than one way. For example, they won't see that 12 rows of 15 can be looked at as 1 hundred and 50 plus 30, or as 120 + 60.

Children who understand this Critical Learning Phase understand the structure of numbers as hundreds, tens, and ones, can show them in arrays, and can partition and describe numbers flexibly with little unnecessary counting.

- **Working with numbers to 1000 or more, describes the number of multiples of tens or hundreds in a number** (*Ex: finds the number of 20s in a number, the number of 50s, the number of 25s*)

  When dividing multi-digit numbers, children need to have a sense of what groups various numbers can be broken into. Their first experiences can be breaking numbers up into multiples of 10 or 100s. This will give them a sense of what is reasonable when they divide with numbers like 35.

  For example:
  Outline an array that shows 120.

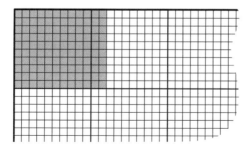

How many 10s are in 120?

How many 20s are in 120?

How many 50s are in 120?

Outline an array that shows 600.

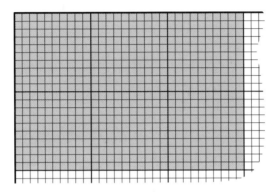

How many 50s are in 600?

How many do you think are in 300?

How many in 900?

Is there a pattern?

Children who understand this Critical Learning Phase divide numbers into multiples of 10 with ease. They build on what they know about 1 hundred and can apply that knowledge to larger numbers.

Appendix

Critical Learning Phases and Word Problems

How Children Learn Number Concepts

APPENDIX
Critical Learning Phases and Solving Word Problems

Children need to develop four aspects to solving word problems. They must be able to: 1) interpret the mathematical situation described in the problem; 2) be able to arrive at the answer in efficient ways, given the numbers presented in the problem; 3) be able to record the problem and their answer(s) using mathematical symbols; and 4) reflect on the answer to be sure it makes sense.

There is a direct correlation between the Critical Learning Phases children understand and their ability to solve word problems. If children are asked to think about numbers at levels they have not reached, they simply will not be able to comprehend what they are being asked to do. For example, if a child is not yet able to answer the question, "How many more in the red train than the blue train?" they will not be able to understand a word problem that asks that same question, such as "Emma picked up 4 shells on the beach. Jamie has 6 shells. How many more shells does Jamie have than Emma?"

The following discussion points out which types of problems are related to particular Critical Learning Phases. Children can experience word problems as part of a group discussion before they reach a certain Critical Learning Phase, but should not be asked to solve them independently. Knowing which type of problem is dependent on understanding a Critical Learning Phase(s) can be helpful in knowing why some of the children in a classroom may not seem to fully understand what is being asked.

The simplest types of word problems for young children are those that describe adding to, taking from, putting together, and taking apart, where the children are asked to find out "how many altogether" or "how many left." Not only are these situations easy for children to understand, but they can also be solved by counting—if the children have not yet developed more sophisticated strategies.

WORKING WITH SINGLE-DIGIT NUMBERS
Counting Objects

Once children are able to count objects within the range of numbers in the problem, they can interpret and solve these types of problems:

Addition

Reggie took a handful of gumdrops. He has 5 red ones and 3 yellow ones. How many does he have altogether?

Four hummingbirds were at the bird feeder. 3 more hummingbirds joined them. How many hummingbirds are there all together?

Subtraction

The clown was holding 7 balloons. He gave 2 of them away. How many does he have left?

Six ladybugs were crawling on a board. All of a sudden, 4 of them flew away. How many ladybugs are still on the board?

Since children can understand what is happening in the problems and can count if necessary to get the answer, these types of problems are appropriate to use when introducing children to the operations of addition and subtraction. These kinds of problems ($3 + 2 = 5$ and $5 - 2 = 3$) are also the easiest for children to interpret when learning to write equations to describe what is happening in the stories.

Number Relationships and Comparing Numbers

Changing Numbers

The following word problems are much harder for children to solve. If the children are unable to change one number to another and describe what they did to change it, they will be unable to independently solve a word problem with that same underlying structure, even with the use of models.

Josh has 5 oranges, but he wants to give an orange to all the members of his team. His team has 8 members. How many more oranges does he need?

There are 6 chairs at the table, but there are 4 people coming. How many chairs does Colin need to take away so he has 4 chairs?

Comparing Numbers

Even though the question is the same for Changing Numbers as for Comparing Numbers (Ex: "How many more?"), the situation is harder for children to understand when asked to compare numbers. That is, the action of comparing two different groups is harder for them to think about than changing one number to another.

You have 6 pieces of gum. I have 3 pieces of gum. How many more do you have than I have? (6 is _____ more than 3).

How Children Learn Number Concepts

Addie read 6 books so far this summer. Molly read 4 books. How many more does Molly need to read to have read the same number as Addie? (4 is ___ less than 6).

Number Composition and Decomposition

Identifying Missing Parts

Even though "taking away" and finding a missing part both require subtraction, a problem that has the action of "taking away" is much easier for young children than a problem with a missing part. For example:

Taking away: 6 birds were in the tree and 4 birds flew away. How many birds are still in the tree?

Missing part: Mimi bought 8 apples from the supermarket. 5 of them are red and the rest are green. How many green apples did Mimi buy?

To solve these "missing part" problems, children need to be able to decompose numbers. They need to be able to think about a whole group where one part is known and the other part is unknown.

There were 6 bananas in the fruit bowl. When Rylie came back later, she could see that there were only 4 left. How many bananas are gone?

Children who know the parts of the numbers used in a word problem will be able to think about problems like this. When they don't know the parts, they have difficulty thinking about what is being asked. Children should be given lots of opportunities to work with numbers less than 5 or 6 until they can solve this kind of problem:

Jon has a box where he keeps his 5 favorite toy animals. Two of the animals are sitting by the box. How many are still in the box?

Multiplication And Division

Understanding the language that describes multiplication and division is so crucial to understanding these processes, I have included the discussion of word problems in Chapter Six: Understanding Multiplication and Division.

WORKING WITH MULTI-DIGIT NUMBERS

The same underlying structures related to the Critical Learning Phases apply to larger numbers as well. Some children find it difficult to interpret word problems using these structures. To help the students interpret the situations, give them problems using smaller numbers.

Number Relationships and Comparing Numbers

Changing Numbers

Peter was delivering milk to the school cafeteria. He needed 550 cartons but he had only 490. How many more cartons of milk does ne need?

Can the children solve this problem if smaller numbers are used?

Peter was delivering milk to the school cafeteria. He needed 20 cartons but he had only 16. How many more cartons of milk does ne need?

Comparing Numbers

The library at Jones Elementary School has 5,486 books. The library at Smith Elementary School has 4,962 books. How many more books does Jones Elementary have than Smith Elementary?

Try smaller numbers to see if the children understand how to compare the numbers.

The library at Jones Elementary School has 90 books. The library at Smith Elementary School has 40 books. How many more books does Jones Elementary have than Smith Elementary?

Number Composition and Decomposition

The high school stadium holds about 10,000 people. The seats on the north side hold about 6,500 people. The rest of the seats are on the south side. How many seats are on the south side of the stadium?

Can the children find parts of the numbers when considering smaller numbers?

The high school stadium holds about 100 people. The seats on the north side hold about 65 people. The rest of the seats are on the south side. How many seats are on the south side of the stadium?

Solving word problems is a perennial challenge for many students. When teachers recognize the relationship of a problem to the development of a Critical Learning Phase, they will be better able to pinpoint the cause of the children's difficulty. They will then be able to provide the kind of instruction that can help their students as well as determine the types of word problems that are appropriate for them.

Math Perspectives
Teacher Development Center

Math Perspectives publishes professional resources and provides long-term professional development and courses for teachers of K-6 mathematics. Learn more about our wide range of professional development institutes, courses, and long-term professional development. Visit mathperspectives.com or call 360-715-2782.

MATH PERSPECTIVES Best-Selling Resources by Kathy Richardson

Assessing Math Concepts Series
- *Counting Objects*
- *Changing Numbers*
- *More/Less Trains*
- *Number Arrangements*
- *Combination Trains*
- *Hiding Assessments*
- *Ten Frames*
- *Grouping Tens*
- *Two-Digit Addition and Subtraction*

Understanding Numbers Series
- *Place Value*
- *Addition and Subtraction*
- *Decimals*

Developing Math Concepts in Pre-Kindergarten

Math Time: The Learning Environment

Professional Development DVDs
- *The Learning Environment for K-2 Mathematics: What Does It Look Like?*
- *Thinking With Numbers: Number Talks*
- *Making it Work in the Classroom*
- *A Look at Children's Thinking*